CW00556143

THE ULTIMATE STAR WARS™ QUIZ BOOK

First published in the UK in 2023 by Studio Press,
an imprint of Bonnier Books UK,
4th Floor, Victoria House, Bloomsbury Square, London. WC1B 4DA
Owned by Bonnier Books,
Sveavägen 56, Stockholm, Sweden

bonnierbooks.co.uk

1 3 5 7 9 10 8 6 4 2

ISBN 978-1-80078-618-9

Written by Paddy Kempshall
Edited by Stephanie Milton
Designed by Maddox Philpot
Production by Giulia Caparrelli

A CIP catalogue record for this book is available from the British Library
Printed avnd bound in Great Britain by Clays Ltd, Elcograf S.p.A

THE ULTIMATE STAR WARS™ QUIZ BOOK

OVER 1,000 QUESTIONS TO TEST YOUR *STAR WARS* KNOWLEDGE!

STUDIO PRESS

CONTENTS

INTRODUCTION

When it comes to *Star Wars*, are you a Jedi Master who knows everything there is to know about a galaxy far, far away? Or are you a youngling who doesn't know the difference between Jedi and Sith?

Well, no matter your level of *Star Wars* knowledge, this is the book for you! Inside these pages, you'll find over 1,000 questions about all things *Star Wars*. From the original trilogy to *The Mandalorian* and everything in between, there are movies, TV series and specialist topics to test your knowledge on.

To make sure there's something for everyone, each of the 24 quiz topics is split into three levels of difficulty: Youngling (easy), Padawan (medium) and Jedi Master (difficult).

If you're a little unsure about your *Star Wars* facts, start off with the Youngling questions for each quiz. The Padawan questions are best suited to those with a decent amount of *Star Wars* knowledge. And if you think you're up for the ultimate challenge, test your skills with the Jedi Master questions.

So get ready to challenge yourself, your friends and your family to find out who will reign supreme as the champion of *The Ultimate* Star Wars *Quiz*!

SECTION ONE:

THE SAGA

1. Which planet has the Trade Federation put under blockade in protest at the taxation of trade routes?
    a. Malastare
    b. Rodia
    c. Lothal
    d. Naboo

2. Which two Jedi are sent to handle the negotiations and settle this dispute?
    a. Yoda and Mace Windu
    b. Ki-Adi Mundi and Obi-Wan Kenobi
    c. Qui-Gon Jinn and Obi-Wan Kenobi
    d. Luminara Unduli and Qui-Gon Jinn

3. Which of these is not a rank in the Jedi order?
    a. Padawan
    b. Knight
    c. Commander
    d. Master

4. What do battle droids often say instead of 'yes'?
    a. Roger, roger!
    b. Aye aye!
    c. Okeydokey!
    d. Yub yub!

5. True or False? Qui-Gon Jinn's lightsaber blade is blue.

6. What is the name of the Queen of Naboo?
    a. Ahsoka
    b. Amidala
    c. Satine
    d. Oola

7. Who does Qui-Gon Jinn run into and fall over as he is fleeing the Trade Federation invasion army?
    a. Hondo Ohnaka
    b. Jar Jar Binks
    c. Obi-Wan Kenobi
    d. Captain Tarpals

8. The chief of the Gungans is Boss ____.
    a. Tarpals
    b. Binks
    c. Nass
    d. Amidala

9. Which planet does Obi-Wan suggest they land on to repair the Queen's ship after it is damaged during her escape?
    a. Mustafar
    b. Kuat
    c. Dantooine
    d. Tatooine

10. Who is Darth Sidious' apprentice?
    a. Darth Bane
    b. Darth Plagueis
    c. Darth Maul
    d. Darth Momin

11. What is the name the Queen uses when she is pretending to be a handmaiden?
    a. Shmi
    b. Padmé
    c. Barriss
    d. Hera

12. Where is Anakin working as a slave when he first meets Qui-Gon?
    a. A podrace pit
    b. A scrapyard
    c. A cantina
    d. A food market

13. What kind of droid is Anakin making to help his mother?
    a. Astromech droid
    b. Power droid
    c. Protocol droid
    d. Battle droid

14. What colours are the sides of the chance cube used to decide if Anakin or his mother will be freed after the podrace?

15. What colour is Sebulba's pod?
    a. Blue
    b. Yellow
    c. Green
    d. Orange

16. How many laps does a racer need to complete to finish the podrace Anakin enters?
    a. 2
    b. 3
    c. 4
    d. 5

17. How many towers are there on the Jedi Temple on Coruscant?
    a. 4
    b. 5
    c. 6
    d. 8

18. Which of these images is **not** one which Anakin correctly identifies during his test by the Jedi Council?
    a. Cup
    b. Speeder
    c. Blaster
    d. Ship

19. Who thinks Anakin is too old to begin his Jedi training?
    a. Qui-Gon Jinn
    b. Mace Windu
    c. Saesee Tiin
    d. Even Piell

20. What is unusual about the lightsaber of the Sith who battles Qui-Gon and Obi-Wan on Naboo?

1. What is the name of the Sith Lord the Trade Federation have made a bargain with to invade Naboo?
    a. Darth Plagueis
    b. Darth Sidious
    c. Darth Bane
    d. Darth Revan

2. What kind of rolling droids do Obi-Wan and Qui-Gon battle on the Trade Federation ship?
    a. Clankers
    b. Gonks
    c. Droidekas
    d. Astromechs

3. Who is Queen Amidala's head of security?
    a. Captain Tarpals
    b. Major Derlin
    c. General Draven
    d. Captain Panaka

4. Which part of the Queen's ship gets damaged as it tries to break through the Trade Federation blockade?
    a. Targeting system
    b. Life support
    c. Shield generator
    d. Main engine

5. Near which settlement does the Queen's ship land on Tatooine?
    a. Mos Espa
    b. Mos Eisley
    c. Mos Pelgo
    d. Anchorhead

6. How do you shut down a pit droid?

7. How much money does Qui-Gon offer to pay for a replacement hyperdrive?
    a. 10,000 republic credits
    b. 20,000 republic credits
    c. 30,000 republic credits
    d. 40,000 republic credits

8. What is Anakin's mother's name?
    a. Shmi
    b. Rio
    c. Dedra
    d. Val

9. What piece of C-3PO has Anakin forgotten to add when Padmé first meets him?

10. What else apart from a droid does Anakin tell Qui-Gon he is building?

11. What does Qui-Gon ask Obi-Wan to measure in Anakin's blood?

12. What is the name of the podrace Anakin enters?
    a. The Krayt Cup
    b. The Tatooine Open
    c. The Mos Espa Classic
    d. The Boonta Eve Classic

13. What does Anakin promise his mother he will do before he leaves with Qui-Gon?
    a. Become a Jedi
    b. Come back and free her
    c. Send for her
    d. Find his father

14. Yoda and which other Jedi sit next to Mace Windu on the Jedi High Council?
    a. Adi Gallia
    b. Ki-Adi Mundi
    c. Plo Koon
    d. Yarael Poof

15. Qui-Gon believes Anakin is destined to fulfil a prophecy to do what?

16. Complete this quote from Yoda: "Fear leads to anger, anger leads to hate, hate leads to ____."

17. Where does Anakin hide during the Battle of Naboo?

18. Who fires the torpedoes which destroy the main reactor on the Droid Control Ship?
    a. R2-D2
    b. Ric Olié
    c. Anakin
    d. Sabé

19. True or False? Obi-Wan uses his own lightsaber to defeat Darth Maul.

20. Who does Palpatine succeed as Supreme Chancellor of the Republic?

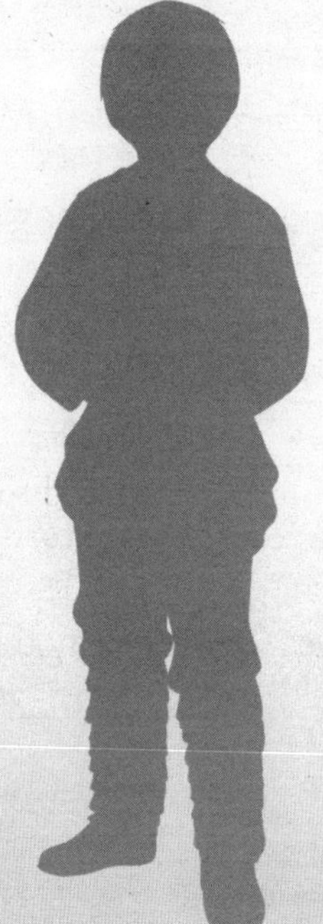

1. What is the designation of the protocol droid which meets Qui-Gon and Obi-Wan aboard the Trade Federation Droid Control ship?

2. What is the name of the Trade Federation Viceroy?

3. What kind of gas do the Trade Federation use to try to neutralise the Jedi?

4. What is the name of the guard who stops Jar Jar as he enters Otoh Gunga?

5. What is the name of the pilot who flew the Queen's ship past the Trade Federation blockade?

6. From what age does Anakin say he can remember being on Tatooine?

7. Who were Anakin and his mother originally sold to as slaves?

8. What kind of hyperdrive generator is Qui-Gon looking to buy from Watto?

9. How much does the food Jar Jar steals on Tatooine cost?

10. On which planet does Qui-Gon say they also have podracing?

11. What was the midi-chlorian count in Anakin's blood?

12. Whose podracers stall at the start of the race?

13. Which bounty hunter is watching the podrace from the cliffs?

14. Name one other person besides Senator Palpatine who is nominated to succeed as Supreme Chancellor?

15. What is the name of the group of Naboo fighters sent to battle the Trade Federation ships?

1. For how long does Supreme Chancellor Palpatine say the Republic has been standing?
    a. 1,000 years
    b. 2,000 years
    c. 5,000 years
    d. 10,000 years

2. Who does Supreme Chancellor Palpatine suggest using as extra security for Senator Amidala?
    a. Yoda
    b. Mace Windu
    c. Obi-Wan Kenobi
    d. Stormtroopers

3. What colour is the speeder Anakin takes to chase after Obi-Wan and the assassin's droid?
    a. Blue
    b. Red
    c. White
    d. Yellow

4. What does Anakin drop during the chase?

5. Who does Padmé appoint as her representative to take her place in the Senate?
    a. Captain Typho
    b. Jar Jar Binks
    c. Boss Nass
    d. R2-D2

6. What does Padmé tell Anakin she thought it was forbidden for a Jedi to do?
    a. Fight
    b. Love
    c. Kill
    d. Hide

7. What does Yoda call young Jedi?

8. Kamino is a planet covered mostly by what?
    a. Gas
    b. Lava
    c. Sand
    d. Oceans

9. What are the Kaminoans creating for the Republic?
    a. Starfighters
    b. Blasters
    c. A clone army
    d. A space station

10. Who does Anakin keep dreaming about that stops him sleeping?
    a. His father
    b. His mother
    c. Darth Sidious
    d. Padmé

11. Who does Anakin go and see first on Tatooine when he is searching for his mother?
    a. Watto
    b. Sebulba
    c. Jabba the Hutt
    d. C-3PO

12. True or False? Anakin's mother is alive when he finds her.

13. How many pillars are in the middle of the arena on Geonosis?
    a. 2
    b. 3
    c. 4
    d. 5

14. What colour is Mace Windu's lightsaber blade?
    a. Blue
    b. Yellow
    c. Green
    d. Purple

15. During the battle on Geonosis, C-3PO complains that he is, "programmed for etiquette, not ____"?
    a. Flying
    b. Battle
    c. Destruction
    d. Spying

16. Who finds Jango Fett's helmet in the arena on Geonosis?
    a. Anakin
    b. Padmé
    c. Boba Fett
    d. Mace Windu

17. What colour are the blaster bolts fired by clone troopers?
    a. Red
    b. Green
    c. Purple
    d. Blue

18. Who falls out of the clone gunship as it is chasing after Count Dooku?
    a. Padmé
    b. Yoda
    c. Obi-Wan
    d. Anakin

19. Which part of Anakin was injured during his duel with Count Dooku?
    a. His left leg
    b. His right arm
    c. His left eye
    d. His right foot

20. On which planet did Anakin and Padmé secretly get married?
    a. Tatooine
    b. Coruscant
    c. Naboo
    d. Geonosis

1. Who is the leader of the Separatist movement?
    a. Nute Gunray
    b. Wat Tambor
    c. Count Dooku
    d. Poggle the Lesser

2. According to Mace Windu, Jedi are "keepers of the peace, not ____"?

3. How long has it been since Anakin last saw Padmé before he and Obi-Wan are assigned to her as security?
    a. 5 years
    b. 10 years
    c. 12 years
    d. 15 years

4. What does someone try and sell Obi-Wan in the club to which they have tracked the person who tried to assassinate Padmé?
    a. Blasters
    b. A lightsaber
    c. A speeder
    d. Death sticks

5. What does Obi-Wan say Jango Fett used to silence Padmé's attacker when they were questioning her?

6. What does Obi-Wan tell Mace Windu and Yoda he thinks Anakin's abilities have made him become?
   a. Reckless
   b. Dangerous
   c. Arrogant
   d. Lazy

7. What is the name of the prime minister of Kamino?
   a. Taun We
   b. Lama Su
   c. Kan Be
   d. Nala Se

8. How many terms did Padmé serve as Queen of Naboo?
   a. 1
   b. 2
   c. 3
   d. 4

9. How many clone soldiers is Obi-Wan told have already been completed by the Kaminoans?
   a. 100,000
   b. 150,000
   c. 200,000
   d. 250,000

10. Who does Jango Fett say hired him to be used in the clone army programme?
    a. Tyranus
    b. Sidious
    c. Plagueis
    d. Bane

11. What weapon does Jango Fett first use to try and destroy Obi-Wan's ship in the asteroids around Geonosis?

12. What relation is Owen Lars to Anakin?
    a. Brother
    b. Cousin
    c. Nephew
    d. Stepbrother

13. According to Cliegg Lars, Anakin's mother had been taken by a "hunting party of ____"?
    a. Jawas
    b. Banthas
    c. Krayt dragons
    d. Tusken Raiders

14. Count Dooku tells Obi-Wan a Sith Lord is now secretly in charge of what?

15. Who proposes the motion to give the Supreme Chancellor emergency powers?
    a. Padmé Amidala
    b. Bail Organa
    c. Jar Jar Binks
    d. Mon Mothma

16. Who is the first person to free themselves from their chains in the Geonosis arena?

17. A hologram of the Geonosian's ultimate weapon can be seen in the background of their control center. What is it?

18. What power does Count Dooku use to disable Anakin in their duel on Geonosis?

19. Who was Count Dooku's Jedi Master?
    a. Mace Windu
    b. Sifo-Dyas
    c. Yoda
    d. Qui-Gon Jinn

20. Who else is present at Anakin and Padmé's secret wedding?

1. What is the name of Senator Amidala's decoy who is killed when her ship is destroyed on a landing pad on Coruscant?

2. Which bounty hunter sends creatures to assassinate Padmé as she is sleeping?

3. Which Jedi is Chief Librarian of the Jedi Archives?

4. According to Obi-Wan's friend, Dex, Kamino is located 12 parsecs outside which area?

5. Who first meets Obi-Wan when he arrives on Kamino?

6. Which Jedi Master supposedly originally asked the Kaminoans to create a clone army?

7. According to Obi-Wan, how long ago did that Jedi Master supposedly die?

8. What kind of creature does Anakin ride on Naboo to try and impress Padmé?

9. With growth acceleration, the clone soldiers are fully grown in how much less time than it would normally take?

10. How far from Tatooine is Geonosis?

11. What is the name of the Geonosian leader?

12. What three kinds of creature are released into the Geonosian arena to attack Anakin, Padmé and Obi-Wan?

13. Who is on a clone gunship with Yoda and Mace when they escape the Geonosian arena?

14. Why is the clone gunship carrying Obi-Wan and Anakin unable to shoot down Count Dooku when they are chasing him?

15. What does Darth Sidious call Count Dooku when he meets him on Coruscant after his escape from Geonosis?

1. What is Anakin's nickname for Ahsoka?
    a. Snaps
    b. Snips
    c. Tups
    d. Tips

2. What is clone CT-27-5555 also known as?
    a. Rex
    b. Hevy
    c. Cody
    d. Fives

3. Clones often refer to battle droids as what?
    a. Scrappers
    b. Clunkers
    c. Clankers
    d. Rogers

4. What is the name of the assassin trained in the dark side by Count Dooku?
    a. Asajj Ventress
    b. Quinlan Vos
    c. Barriss Offee
    d. Luminara Unduli

5. Who disguises themselves as a Jedi in order to rescue Padmé when she is taken as a hostage for the Separatists on Rodia?
    a. C-3PO
    b. Jar Jar
    c. Rex
    d. Aurra Sing

6. What is the name of the virus the Separatists are secretly developing on Naboo?
    a. Red Moon Virus
    b. Blue Shadow Virus
    c. Green Phantom Virus
    d. Yellow Mist Virus

7. Jedi holocrons can only be opened by using what?
    a. A lightsaber
    b. A key
    c. The Force
    d. Credits

8. The Death Watch is a violent splinter group originating from which planet?
    a. Cato Neimoidia
    b. Saleucami
    c. Mandalore
    d. Felucia

9. Which ancient weapon does Pre Vizsla wield?
    a. A lightsaber
    b. The Darksaber
    c. An electro-whip
    d. A beskar spear

10. Who poses as a clone cadet to sneak aboard a Jedi cruiser in order to try and assassinate Mace Windu?
    a. Asajj Ventress
    b. Gar Saxon
    c. Boba Fett
    d. Bo-Katan Kryze

11. What type of clone trooper is considered by clones to be the best of the best?
    a. Rocket troopers
    b. Scout troopers
    c. Aqua troopers
    d. ARC troopers

12. Who does Count Dooku take as an apprentice after Asajj Ventress leaves him?
    a. Savage Opress
    b. Darth Maul
    c. Embo
    d. Hondo Ohnaka

13. Which Wookiee captive teams up with Ahsoka on Wasskah after being captured by Trandoshan hunters?
    a. Tarfful
    b. Chewbacca
    c. Black Krrsantan
    d. Attichitcuk

14. Which alien race does Yoda call on to help repel the Separatist attack on the Mon Calamari home world?
    a. Wookiees
    b. Sullustans
    c. Gungans
    d. Jawas

15. How many arms does Jedi General Pong Krell have?
    a. 2
    b. 3
    c. 4
    d. 5

16. R2-D2 becomes part of which special droid squadron on a mission to steal a Separatist encryption module?
    a. A-Squad
    b. B-Squad
    c. C-Squad
    d. D-Squad

17. What is the name of the alliance of criminal syndicates which is assembled by Maul?
    a. Ghost Collective
    b. Phantom Collective
    c. Shadow Collective
    d. Dark Collective

18. Who sets up Ahsoka to take the blame for the bombing of the Jedi Temple and the deaths of several clones?
    a. Barriss Offee
    b. Savage Opress
    c. Asajj Ventress
    d. Pre Vizsla

19. What colour are the blades on the lightsaber pikes of Jedi Temple guards?
    a. Yellow
    b. Red
    c. Blue
    d. Green

20. What gift does Anakin give Ahsoka before the Siege of Mandalore?
    a. A helmet
    b. A blaster
    c. Her lightsabers
    d. A speeder bike

1. Which Jedi are sent to guard Nute Gunray as he is being transported to Coruscant after his capture?
    a. Obi-Wan and Anakin
    b. Luminara and Ahsoka
    c. Anakin and Ahsoka
    d. Adi Gallia and Luminara

2. What does Hondo Ohnaka demand as payment from the Republic in return for handing over Count Dooku?
    a. 1 million credits in spice
    b. 2 million credits in spice
    c. 1 million credits in kyber crystals
    d. 2 million credits in kyber crystals

3. What nickname do clone troopers use for the weapon they use to ionise and stun droids?

4. Who is the leader of the Twi'lek resistance on Ryloth?
    a. Saw Gerrera
    b. Cham Syndulla
    c. Lux Bonteri
    d. Rako Hardeen

5. Cad Bane's band of bounty hunters take hostages in the Senate Building to force the release of who?
    a. Jabba the Hutt
    b. Ziro the Hutt
    c. Lom Pyke
    d. Gha Nachkt

6. Which Jedi does Ahsoka ask to help find her lightsaber after it is stolen on Coruscant?
    a. Jocasta Nu
    b. Plo Koon
    c. Tera Sinube
    d. Kit Fisto

7. To which moon were the members of Death Watch exiled?

8. What is the Republic's new weapon which is used by Obi-Wan at Christophsis to break Admiral Trench's blockade?

9. What was the name of the squad of clone trainees which Echo and Fives belonged to?
    a. Torrent
    b. Bantha
    c. Domino
    d. Gundark

10. Which bounty hunter does Ahsoka have repeated Force visions of before her trip to Alderaan with Padmé?
    a. Boba Fett
    b. Aurra Sing
    c. Bossk
    d. Embo

11. Who is the spiritual guide of the Nightsisters of Dathomir?

12. Where does Anakin encounter the Father, the Son and the Daughter?
    a. Mortis
    b. Saleucami
    c. Orto Plutonia
    d. Moraband

13. Obi-Wan and Anakin are sent to free Jedi General Even Piell from which impenetrable prison?

14. Which clone sacrifices himself to destroy the Separatist supply ship over Umbara?
    a. Hevy
    b. Hardcase
    c. Tup
    d. Cutup

15. How many colonists are enslaved by Zygerrians on Kiros?
    a. 10,000
    b. 25,000
    c. 50,000
    d. 100,000

16. To which planet do youngling Jedi go to complete the challenge of the Gathering?

17. Who is Bo-Katan's sister?

18. To which planet do the Bad Batch track the Separatist signal broadcasting Rex's stolen strategic algorithm?
    a. Christophsis
    b. Onderon
    c. Florrum
    d. Skako Minor

19. What does Anakin tell Ahsoka means everything to the clones?

20. Who comes back to the moon where Ahsoka leaves her lightsaber and retrieves it?

1. What is Clone Captain Rex's clone trooper number?

2. Clone Commander Cody is the leader of which clone attack battalion?

3. Which Jedi Master originally brought Ahsoka to the Jedi Temple when she was young?

4. In the Twi'lek language, what does "Nerra" mean?

5. Jedi Master Mace Windu removes Ahsoka from battlefield duties for disobeying orders in the battle on which planet?

6. Bolla Ropal was the keeper of what?

7. When he was younger, how long did Obi-Wan spend on a mission protecting Duchess Satine?

8. Who is the first senator to die in suspicious circumstances during a crucial vote on ending Republic military production for the war?

9. Who suggests that the armour of the Zillo beast could be useful to the Republic military?

10. Jedi Quinlan Vos has a mysterious ability to glean what information from objects?

11. What is the fake name Anakin uses when he is pretending to be a Zygerrian slaver?

12. What does the youngling Gungi find within himself during his challenge in The Gathering?

13. Which droid oversees the younglings in the construction of their lightsabers?

14. Which clone trooper succumbs to a mysterious mental illness that leads to the death of Jedi Master Tiplar?

15. What is Anakin's passcode which Ahsoka uses to access the file on Rex's grievance report on the death of Fives?

1. Who is the cyborg leader of the Separatists?

2. Which person, who has been kidnapped by the Separatists, are Obi-Wan and Anakin sent to rescue?
   a. Padmé
   b. Yoda
   c. Chancellor Palpatine
   d. Mace Windu

3. How many eyes does a buzz droid have?
   a. 1
   b. 2
   c. 3
   d. 4

4. What does R2-D2 cover the droids in that capture him aboard the Separatist ship?
   a. Water
   b. Smoke
   c. Paint
   d. Oil

5. Which type of weapon does General Grievous collect?

6. What does Padmé tell Anakin when he returns from the rescue mission?
   a. She is going to Naboo
   b. He needs to go to Tatooine
   c. He is getting a medal
   d. She is pregnant

7. True or False? The Jedi Council make Anakin a Jedi Master.

8. To which planet does General Grievous flee after the Battle of Coruscant?
   a. Mustafar
   b. Utapau
   c. Christophsis
   d. Felucia

9. According to Chancellor Palpatine, the dark side of the Force is a pathway to many abilities some consider to be what?
   a. Too powerful
   b. A myth
   c. Dangerous
   d. Unnatural

10. How many lightsabers does General Grievous use in his battle against Obi-Wan?
   a. 1
   b. 2
   c. 3
   d. 4

11. Which part of General Grievous does Obi-Wan expose when he forces open his armour?

12. Who does Anakin first tell that he thinks Chancellor Palpatine is actually a Sith Lord?
    a. Mace Windu
    b. Obi-Wan Kenobi
    c. Padmé
    d. Yoda

13. What colour is the blade of Darth Sidious' lightsaber?

14. What name does Darth Sidious give Anakin when he becomes his apprentice?

15. Where does Anakin go to wipe out the Jedi?
    a. The Temple
    b. The spaceport
    c. The Senate
    d. The mountains

16. True or False? Anakin lets the youngling Jedi escape.

17. Who travels with Anakin to Mustafar?
    a. C-3PO
    b. Obi-Wan
    c. Darth Sidious
    d. R2-D2

18. When they battle each other, who ignites their lightsaber first, Anakin or Obi-Wan?

19. What does Padmé name her children?

20. After being rescued from Mustafar, Darth Vader and Darth Sidious observe the construction of which object being built in space?

1. What colour is the starfighter Anakin flies during the Battle of Coruscant?

2. During the battle, Obi-Wan says, "Flying is for ____"?
   a. Jedi
   b. Droids
   c. Younglings
   d. Mynocks

3. How do you shut down a buzz droid?

4. During the rescue, what does Obi-Wan tell Chancellor Palpatine is his and Anakin's specialty?

5. Who orders Anakin to finish Count Dooku after he has surrendered?
   a. Chancellor Palpatine
   b. General Grievous
   c. Obi-Wan Kenobi
   d. Nute Gunray

6. On which planet does Padmé say she would like the baby to be born?

7. Who tells Anakin where General Grievous is hiding?
   a. Obi-Wan
   b. Padmé
   c. Yoda
   d. Chancellor Palpatine

8. According to Anakin, what do Sith rely on for their strength?
    a. Anger
    b. Fear
    c. Hatred
    d. Passion

9. Chancellor Palpatine tells Anakin the story of which Sith Lord?
    a. Darth Sidious
    b. Darth Bane
    c. Darth Plagueis
    d. Darth Tyranus

10. Who does General Grievous say trained him in the Jedi arts?
    a. Yoda
    b. Qui-Gon Jinn
    c. Darth Maul
    d. Count Dooku

11. How many blaster shots does it take Obi-Wan to defeat General Grievous?
    - a. 1
    - b. 3
    - c. 5
    - d. 7

12. When the Jedi come to arrest him, what does Chancellor Palpatine accuse them of?
    - a. Cowardice
    - b. Murder
    - c. Treason
    - d. Sabotage

13. What is the name of the secret order to attack the Jedi which Darth Sidious gives to the clone army?

14. Who arrives at the Jedi Temple while the Jedi are being attacked by clone soldiers?

15. Which two Wookiees help Yoda escape the clone attack on Kashyyyk?

16. Who picks up the emergency message Obi-Wan sends as he is leaving Utapau?
    - a. Yoda
    - b. Mace Windu
    - c. Padmé
    - d. Bail Organa

17. What does Chancellor Palpatine announce that the Republic will be reformed into?

18. Obi-Wan tells Anakin that he was supposed to "bring balance to Force, not leave it in ___".

19. Which of Padmé's children is born first?

20. Darth Sidious tells Anakin that Padmé was killed by whom?

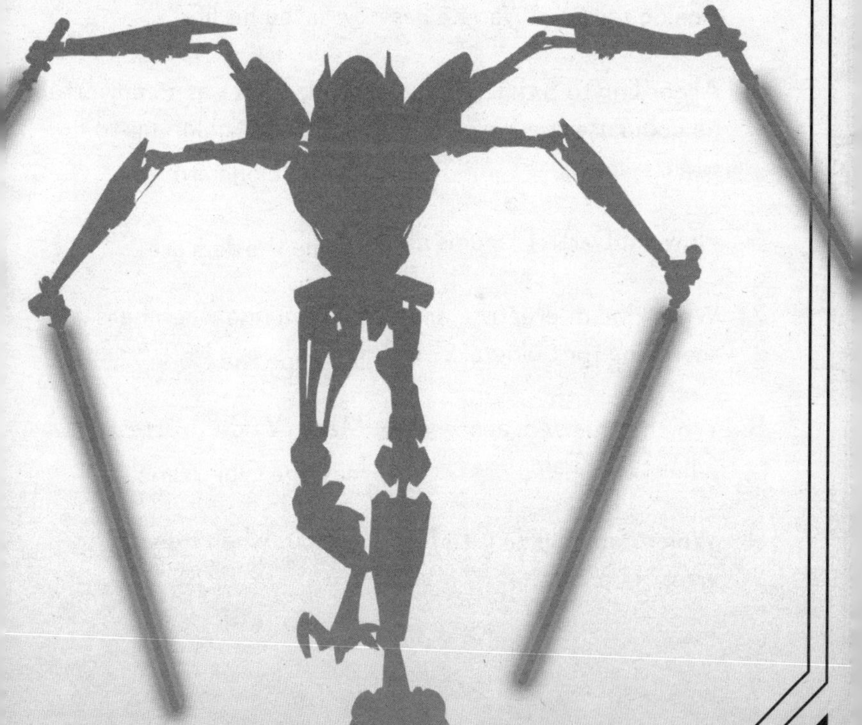

1. What is the name of the pilot leading the clone squadron accompanying Anakin and Obi-Wan at the Battle of Coruscant?

2. Complete the quote from Count Dooku to Anakin before their battle: "Twice the ____, double the fall."

3. What does General Grievous use to trap the Jedi and Chancellor Palpatine before they can escape his ship?

4. After the Battle of Coruscant, how many times does Anakin tell Obi-Wan he has now saved his life?

5. According to Sith legend, Darth Plagueis was so powerful he could use the Force to influence midi-chlorians to do what?

6. How did Darth Plagueis die?

7. What kind of creature does Obi-Wan ride when he is searching for General Grievous on Utapau?

8. Which three Jedi accompany Mace Windu to arrest Chancellor Palpatine?

9. Which Jedi falls first to Darth Sidious when they try to arrest him?

10. On Utapau, who returns Obi-Wan's lost lightsaber to him?

11. What emergency code does Obi-Wan broadcast as he escapes from Utapau?

12. On which planet is Ki-Adi Mundi attacked and defeated by his clone army?

13. Which Jedi is shot down by clones in his fighter over Cato Neimoidia?

14. What is the name of the place where Luke and Leia are born?

15. Who does Yoda tell Obi-Wan he will teach him to communicate with while he is in hiding on Tatooine?

1. What is the Bad Batch's official squad name?
    a. Clone Force 11
    b. Clone Force 33
    c. Clone Force 66
    d. Clone Force 99

2. According to Crosshair "good soldiers ____."
    a. Fight hard
    b. Don't quit
    c. Follow orders
    d. Work together

3. Whose malfunctioning inhibitor chip is discovered first?
    a. Hunter
    b. Crosshair
    c. Wrecker
    d. Tech

4. What is the name of the Imperial admiral who implements the chain code project?
    a. Yularen
    b. Motti
    c. Piett
    d. Rampart

5. Which of Echo's contacts does he think can let the Bad Batch know why a bounty hunter is targeting Omega?
    a. Cid
    b. Nala Se
    c. Cham Syndulla
    d. Saw Gerrera

6. Who battles a rancor into exhaustion?
    a. Hunter
    b. Echo
    c. Wrecker
    d. Crosshair

7. Which bounty hunter do the Bad Batch encounter on Bracca?
    a. Aurra Sing
    b. Boba Fett
    c. Bossk
    d. Cad Bane

8. True or False? Lama Su wants to keep Omega alive after retrieving her from the bounty hunter.

9. What are the creatures in the caverns under Cid's parlor scared away by?
    a. Sound
    b. Light
    c. Spice
    d. Silence

10. How many TK troopers are being trained at the Imperial base on Daro?
    a. 100
    b. 500
    c. 1000
    d. 2000

11. Which member of the Bad Batch gets captured by Imperial troops on Daro?
    a. Hunter
    b. Echo
    c. Omega
    d. Tech

12. True or False? Crosshair eventually has his inhibitor chip removed.

13. Hunter tells Crosshair that as far as the Empire are concerned "All you'll ever be to them is a ___."
    a. Soldier
    b. Number
    c. Clone
    d. Liability

14. Whose war chest are the Bad Batch sent to steal from Serenno?
    a. General Grievous
    b. Asajj Ventress
    c. Wat Tambor
    d. Count Dooku

15. Phee thinks the "Heart of the ___" is hidden on Skara Nal.
    a. Mountain
    b. Galaxy
    c. Jedi
    d. Sith

16. What is the name of the Wookiee Force user the Bad Batch rescue from Spaceport Vanguard Axis?
    a. Gungi
    b. Gingi
    c. Gongi
    d. Gangi

17. Who saves Senator Chuchi from an assassin on Coruscant?
    a. Omega
    b. Cody
    c. Rex
    d. Hunter

18. Which Bad Batch member leaves with Rex to continue the fight and do more for the clones?
    a. Tech
    b. Echo
    c. Wrecker
    d. Hunter

19. The people in Mokko's mine compete to become top earner for what reward?
    a. Money
    b. Power
    c. Food
    d. Water

20. Which member of the Bad Batch sacrifices themself so the rest of the squad can escape from Governor Tarkin's compound?
    a. Crosshair
    b. Hunter
    c. Wrecker
    d. Tech

1. What is the name of the Bad Batch's ship?
   a. *Gauntlet*
   b. *Marauder*
   c. *Scythe*
   d. *Blade*

2. Who comes to Tipoca City to tell the Kaminoans that their deal to create a clone army is over?
   a. The Emperor
   b. Darth Vader
   c. Admiral Tarkin
   d. Admiral Rampart

3. What kind of creature attacks Omega after she wanders from a farm on Saleucami to get a ball?
   a. Reek
   b. Acklay
   c. Nexu
   d. Gundark

4. Who hires Cid to recover Muchi?
   a. Cad Bane
   b. Bib Fortuna
   c. Taun We
   d. Isa Durand

5. What does Cid send the Bad Batch to steal from a droid decommissioning facility on Corellia?

6. What snack do Wrecker and Omega like to share after missions?

7. Who is sent by the Kaminoans to retrieve Omega from Cad Bane?
    a. Nala Se
    b. Taun We
    c. Lama Su
    d. Admiral Rampart

8. What has the Empire built on Ryloth?

9. What is the name of the Twi'lek senator from Ryloth?
    a. Cham Syndulla
    b. Orn Free Taa
    c. Lyn Me
    d. Bib Fortuna

10. What piece of tech does Crosshair use to try and draw the rest of the Bad Batch into a trap on Kamino?

11. Who frees Omega's medical capsule from the wreckage while trying to escape the destruction of Tipoca City?

12. What is Tech teaching Omega about?
    a. Imperial fleet ship types
    b. Imperial battle tactics
    c. Imperial troop formations
    d. Imperial politics

13. What is the Bad Batch's plan code for radio silence between teams?

14. On the Safa Toma Speedway, no one ever takes the tunnel on which side of Gambler's Gulch?

15. What are the Bad Batch delivering to the Vanguard Axis droid cartel at Ordo Tera Spaceport?
    a. Spice
    b. Forged chain codes
    c. Forged Imperial currency
    d. Weapons

16. What important bill is the Senate debating in the aftermath of Kamino's destruction?

17. Who does Slip contact about escaping from Coruscant?
    a. Ahsoka
    b. Cody
    c. Rex
    d. Hunter

18. Chuchi is the senator for which system?

19. After the destruction of Kamino, Emperor Palpatine calls for the passing of new legislation and the creation of what?
    a. Imperial clone troopers
    b. Imperial stormtroopers
    c. Imperial Star Destroyers
    d. Imperial TIE fighters

20. What fearsome creature do the Bad Batch discover the Empire is cloning?

1. Who is Depa Billaba's Padawan?

2. How many more successful missions does Wrecker put on the board when the Bad Batch return to Kamino after Order 66 is implemented?

3. What is the name of Wrecker's Tooka doll?

4. What is the name of the project which creates new elite squads of troopers under Crosshair's command?

5. On which planet do the Bad Batch meet Rex to get their inhibitor chips removed?

6. What codename did the Kaminoans use for Boba Fett when he was cloned?
7. Omega pays off the Bad Batch's debts by playing which game for money?

8. Who sent Hera to gather intel from the Imperial refinery on Ryloth?

9. How long was Crosshair trapped on Kamino after its bombardment before being rescued?

10. What is Cid's full name?

11. Phee tells a story in Cid's parlour about fending off what creature bare-handed?

12. What is the name of the bar on Coruscant where clone troopers go to drink?

13. On which Coruscant level do the Bad Batch meet Rex and Chuchi?

14. What is the name of the doctor in charge of the facility on Tantiss?

15. Governor Tarkin hosts a high-level Imperial summit at his compound on which planet?

1. On which planet did Han grow up?
    a. Corellia
    b. Coruscant
    c. Kijimi
    d. Glee Anselm

2. What is the name of Han's childhood friend when he was growing up in the gangs?
    a. Val
    b. Zorii
    c. Qi'ra
    d. Maz

3. What does Han pretend is a thermal detonator when he is threatening the head of his gang?
    a. A rock
    b. A ball
    c. A shoe
    d. A coin

4. What does Han say he's going to become when he leaves his homeworld?
    a. A gambler
    b. A smuggler
    c. A podracer
    d. A pilot

5. What does Han give his friend in the queue as they are trying to get through the checkpoint at the spaceport?
    a. Money
    b. A blaster
    c. Lucky dice
    d. A coat

6. What does Han steal from a child in the spaceport to use as a disguise?
    a. A coat
    b. A hat
    c. A blanket
    d. A scarf

7. What is the name of the person Han meets who is leading a gang pulling a job on Mimban?
    a. Calrissian
    b. Dryden
    c. Tarkin
    d. Beckett

8. What species is 'the beast' that Han is to be fed to on Mimban?
    a. Ardennian
    b. Wookiee
    c. Rancor
    d. Duros

9. True or False? Han can speak the same language as 'the beast'.

10. Han and 'the beast' are chained together by which body parts?
    a. Their arms
    b. Their legs
    c. Their waists
    d. Their necks

11. Who does Qi'ra take Han to see about getting a ship to help with their job?
    a. Rio
    b. Dryden
    c. Lando
    d. Chewbacca

12. After gambling and losing against him, when talking to Qi'ra, Han calls his opponent "Captain ___".
    a. Lucky
    b. Panic
    c. Wonderful
    d. Cheater

13. What is the ship called that Qi'ra's friend says they can use on their job?

14. The lesson that Beckett tries to teach Chewbacca when playing dejarik is that "people are ___".
    a. Untrustworthy
    b. Selfish
    c. Dangerous
    d. Predictable

15. What pieces of Lando's clothing does Han find Qi'ra trying on aboard the ship?
    a. Shirts
    b. Trousers
    c. Hats
    d. Capes

16. As part of the plan to get into the mines on Kessel, who pretends to be slaves?
    a. Qi'ra and Han
    b. Beckett and Chewbacca
    c. Chewbacca and Han
    d. Han and Lando

17. What does L3-37 remove from the droid in the Kessel control room?
    a. Restraining bolt
    b. Leg
    c. Arm
    d. Aerial

18. How many canisters does Han need to steal from the mines?
    a. 10
    b. 12
    c. 14
    d. 16

19. Who double-crosses Han with the head of Crimson Dawn?
    a. Qi'ra
    b. Lando
    c. Chewbacca
    d. Beckett

20. In their final confrontation, who shoots first; Han or Beckett?

1. What is the name of the gang Han was part of when he was growing up on Corellia?
    a. Crimson Dawn
    b. White Fangs
    c. White Worms
    d. Red Gundarks

2. Who is the enforcer who takes Han to see the head of the gang after his job goes wrong?
    a. Rio
    b. Grevel
    c. Kragan
    d. Moloch

3. From which spaceport do Han and Qi'ra plan to leave Corellia?
    a. Spellhaus
    b. Fondor
    c. Coronet
    d. Mos Espa

4. How many patrol troopers give chase to Han's speeder on the way to the spaceport?
    a. 1
    b. 2
    c. 3
    d. 4

5. At the spaceport, the recruitment advertisement for the Imperial Army says recruits can bring "____ and unity" to the galaxy.
    a. Strength
    b. Order
    a. Peace
    b. Control

6. According to the recruiter, which part of the Imperial Army do most recruits end up in?

7. Han tells Beckett he was kicked out of the Imperial Academy for having what?
    a. A smart mouth
    b. A mind of his own
    c. A bad attitude
    d. Bad luck

8. At the battle of Mimban, Beckett is disguised as an Imperial Officer of which rank?
    a. Lieutenant
    b. Captain
    c. Commander
    d. Major

9. In the pit, Han calls 'the beast' a "mangy Kashyyykian ——!"
    a. Nerf herder
    b. Moof-milker
    c. Laser brain
    d. Fuzzball

10. Who does Val tell Beckett they should be worrying about when pulling their job on Vandor?
    a. Dryden Vos
    b. Enfys Nest
    c. Saw Gerrera
    d. Anto Kreegyr

11. Which organisation actually hired Beckett's team for the job on Vandor?
    a. Crimson Dawn
    b. Black Sun
    c. Pyke Syndicate
    d. Hutt Cartel

12. What is Beckett's first name?

13. Where does Qi'ra suggest that they could find unrefined coaxium?
    a. Exegol
    b. Castilon
    c. Rodia
    d. Kessel

14. Who is Lando's droid co-pilot on the *Millennium Falcon*?
    a. D-O
    b. L3-37
    c. MSE-6
    d. R5-D4

15. To what percentage does Beckett reduce Lando's cut for the Kessel job in return for freeing the *Millennium Falcon* from impound?
    a. 10%
    b. 20%
    c. 25%
    d. 30%

16. Who does Lando's droid companion tell Qi'ra she thinks he has feelings for?
    a. Han
    b. Lando
    c. Val
    d. Beckett

17. What does Qi'ra offer the Director on Kessel in return for the coaxium?
    a. Credits
    b. Weapons
    c. Ships
    d. Slaves

18. Lando says it's impossible to make the Kessel Run in less than how many parsecs?
    a. 15
    b. 20
    c. 25
    d. 30

19. Who is the ultimate head of Crimson Dawn?

20. What is the name of the game Han plays with Lando to win the *Millennium Falcon* from him?

1. What is the name of the creature in charge of Han's gang on Corellia?

2. Where does the head of the White Worms say they rescued Qi'ra from when she was younger?

3. What model number of speeder does Han use to escape to the spaceport on Corellia?

4. Who is Qi'ra scared she and Han might get sold to if traffickers catch them out in the galaxy?

5. Val tells Beckett she wants to get the Xan sisters or who else on the Vandor job instead of Han and Chewbacca?

6. Beckett says he wants to retire and learn to play which kind of instrument?

7. Which Imperial vaults does Qi'ra suggest might hold the amount of refined coaxium they need?

8. Which group controls the spice mines on Kessel?

9. Where does Chewbacca suggest that they can get their coaxium refined for Crimson Dawn?

10. What kind of ship does Han pretend he has when he first gambles against Lando?

11. Which card does Han say Lando used to cheat with in their first game?

12. According to Lando, what route do you need to take to get to Kessel?

13. What fighting technique does Qi'ra use to defeat the mine director on Kessel?

14. How old does Chewbacca tell Han he is?

15. How much is the coaxium that Han gives Enfys Nest worth?

1. How long has Obi-Wan been on Tatooine guarding Luke?
   a. 5 years
   b. 10 years
   c. 15 years
   d. 20 years

2. How many Inquisitors arrive on Tatooine on a hunt?
   a. 1
   b. 2
   c. 3
   d. 4

3. What do the Inquisitors hunt for the Empire?
   a. Rebels
   b. Bounty hunters
   c. Aliens
   d. Jedi

4. What colour is Reva's lightsaber blade?
   a. Green
   b. Blue
   c. Red
   d. Yellow

5. Who does the Grand Inquisitor tell Reva she has a fixation with?
   a. Darth Vader
   b. Anakin Skywalker
   c. Obi-Wan Kenobi
   d. Yoda

6. What does Obi-Wan take home from work every day, hidden in his apron?
    a. Water
    b. Meat
    c. Money
    d. Sand

7. When he meets a fugitive Jedi in the Tatooine desert, what does Obi-Wan tell them is his name?
    a. Ben
    b. Qui-Gon
    c. Owen
    d. Luke

8. What does Leia call her little flying droid?
    a. Lily
    b. Luke
    c. Lola
    d. Lolly

9. True or False? Obi-Wan immediately agrees to help find Leia.

10. What does Leia want Obi-Wan to use the Force to do?
    a. Make her disappear
    b. Make her taller
    c. Make her float
    d. Make her forget

11. What does Obi-Wan use to save Leia when she falls from the roof after her rescue?
    a. A ladder
    b. Rope
    c. A net
    d. The Force

12. When Reva is stalking Obi-Wan on Daiyu, what is it that she says betrays him?
    a. His fear
    b. His anger
    c. His pride
    d. His hate

13. Who does Reva tell Obi-Wan she wants to take him to after capturing him?
    a. The Grand Inquisitor
    b. Lord Vader
    c. The Emperor
    d. Fifth Brother

14. Freck, the transport driver on Mapuzo who picks up Obi-Wan and Leia also gives a lift to a group of which other people?
    a. Stormtroopers
    b. Farmers
    c. Inquisitors
    d. Rebels

15. What is the name of the secret network that helps Force-sensitive people and Jedi flee from the Empire?
    a. The Way
    b. The Path
    c. The Tunnel
    d. The Road

16. Who is waiting for Leia at end of the escape tunnel on Mapuzo?
    a. Obi-Wan
    b. Reva
    c. Darth Vader
    d. Tala

17. Where does Reva place the tracker to follow Obi-Wan and Leia after they escape from the Inquisitors' base?
    a. In Lola
    b. On Leia
    c. In a speeder
    d. On Obi-Wan

18. Who goes into the vents to try and repair the hangar doors so everyone can escape from Darth Vader?
    a. Obi-Wan
    b. Tala
    c. Lola
    d. Leia

19. True or False? Reva was a youngling at the Jedi Temple on the night of Order 66.

20. What does Darth Vader bury Obi-Wan under during their final battle?
    a. Water
    b. Sand
    c. Rocks
    d. Metal

1. What does the Grand Inquisitor say is the key to hunting Jedi?
    a. Patience
    b. Speed
    c. Fear
    d. Anger

2. What is Reva's name amongst the Inquisitors?
    a. Second Sister
    b. Third Sister
    c. Fourth Sister
    d. Seventh Sister

3. As well as something to repair his moisture vaporator, what else does Obi-Wan buy from the Jawa that visits him in his home?
    a. A belt
    b. A T-16 skyhopper toy
    c. A droid
    d. A hydrospanner

4. What is the name of the Jedi the Inquisitors are looking for on Tatooine?
    a. Nari
    b. Nomi
    c. Nami
    d. Nimi

5. Owen tells Reva he thinks that "Jedi are ____".
    a. Heroes
    b. Traitors
    c. Vermin
    d. Animals

6. Leia's cousin accuses her of not being a real what?
    a. Senator
    b. Friend
    c. Organa
    d. Rebel

7. What is in the box Obi-Wan digs up in the sands of Tatooine?

8. Who are Leia's kidnappers actually working for?
    a. Darth Vader
    b. The Grand Inquisitor
    c. Fifth Brother
    d. Reva

9. What does someone try to sell Obi-Wan when he arrives on Daiyu?
    a. Food
    b. Information
    c. Death Sticks
    d. Spice

10. What is the name of the fake Jedi on Daiyu?
    a. Nari
    b. Haja
    c. Roken
    d. Breha

11. After he rescues Leia, Obi-Wan tells her to say they are farmers from which planet?
    a. Mustafar
    b. Tatooine
    c. Jabiim
    d. Tawl

12. What does Reva tell Obi-Wan that comes as a surprise to him?

13. Who does Obi-Wan think he sees in the hills on Mapuzo?
    a. Qui-Gon Jinn
    b. Yoda
    c. Anakin Skywalker
    d. Mace Windu

14. What is the name of the Imperial Officer who is Obi-Wan's contact on Mapuzo?

15. Complete the inscription Obi-Wan finds on the wall of the Mapuzo safehouse: "Only when the ____ are closed can you truly see."

16. What does Obi-Wan discover is being kept beneath the Inquisitors' base?

17. Which pilot doesn't survive the rescue from the Inquisitors' base?
    a. Sully
    b. Wade
    c. Roken
    d. Wedge

18. What colour breaker does Leia need to find to open the hanger doors on Jabiim?

19. What does Obi-Wan give Leia that used to belong to the Imperial Officer who helped them escape?
    a. A droid
    b. A blaster
    c. A holster
    d. A communicator

20. Who appears to Obi-Wan when he is travelling home after meeting Luke at the Lars farm?

1. Obi-Wan works on Tatooine harvesting the meat from what kind of creature?

2. What is Leia's adopted mother's name?

3. What is the name of the person in charge of the group who abducts Leia?

4. Who does Obi-Wan find begging for money on the streets of Daiyu?

5. How many credits does Haja want to help find Leia?

6. What does Haja give Obi-Wan which contains the coordinates he needs to get to Mapuzo?

7. Obi-Wan tells Leia that Mapuzo is what kind of system?

8. What is the name of the Inquisitors' headquarters?

9. On Mapuzo, Leia tells the speeder driver they flag down that her name is what?

10. In the Mapuzo safehouse, Obi-Wan finds evidence that which Jedi survived Order 66?

11. What does Darth Vader set fire to on Mapuzo to burn Obi-Wan?

12. Who is the leader of 'the Path' on Jabiim?

13. Tala tells Reva 'the Path' is run out of which planet?

14. An incident on which planet made Tala want to fight against Empire?

15. When preparing for Reva's attack, who does Owen tell Luke might attack the farm?

1. What is Ezra's full name?
    a. Ezra Syndulla
    b. Ezra Wren
    c. Ezra Jarrus
    d. Ezra Bridger

2. On which planet does Ezra live?
    a. Garel
    b. Lothal
    c. Alderaan
    d. Malachor

3. Which member of the *Ghost*'s crew wears Mandalorian armour?
    a. Zeb
    b. Hera
    c. Sabine
    d. Ezra

4. Ezra discovers that Kanan's holocron contains a message from whom?
    a. Yoda
    b. Obi-Wan Kenobi
    c. Ahsoka Tano
    d. Luminara Unduli

5. What is the codename of Hera's secret contact?
    a. Fulcrum
    b. Spectre
    c. Phantom
    d. Ghost

6. Who does Ezra see apparently kill Kanan inside the Jedi Temple?
    a. Darth Vader
    b. The Emperor
    c. The Grand Inquisitor
    d. Savage Opress

7. What colour is the blade of Ezra's first lightsaber?
    a. Green
    b. Blue
    c. Yellow
    d. White

8. True or False? Senator Trayvis tells Ezra that his parents are still alive.

9. What is the name of the A-wing squadron that often works with the *Ghost* on missions?
    a. Mynock squadron
    b. Loth-bat squadron
    c. Phoenix Squadron
    d. Krayt squadron

10. Who joins the crew of the *Ghost* to help battle Darth Vader in space during the Siege of Lothal?
    a. Luke Skywalker
    b. Lando Calrissian
    c. Ahsoka Tano
    d. R2-D2

11. What does Ezra feel when he senses Darth Vader in the Force?
    a. Fear
    b. Anger
    c. Hate
    d. Cold

12. Which Inquisitor is sent in place of Darth Vader to continue the hunt for the rebels?
    a. Third Brother
    b. Fourth Brother
    c. Fifth Brother
    d. Sixth Brother

13. Which agent does Bail Organa send to Lothal on a mission to deliver some cruisers to the rebels?
    a. R2-D2
    b. C-3PO
    c. Leia
    d. Fulcrum

14. Zeb gets stranded on a frozen moon of Geonosis with which member of the Empire?
    a. Darth Vader
    b. Agent Kallus
    c. Governor Pryce
    d. Admiral Konstantine

15. Who does the mysterious figure that Ezra meets in the Sith Temple turn out to be?
    a. Ahsoka
    b. Darth Vader
    c. Maul
    d. Rukh

16. Who is the blue-skinned Imperial commander sent to Lothal to deal with the rebels?
    a. Grand Admiral Thrawn
    b. Admiral Konstantine
    c. Admiral Titus
    d. Vice Admiral Rampart

17. Maul asks Obi-Wan if he's protecting who on Tatooine?
    a. The Chosen One
    b. The Son
    c. Bendu
    d. Fulcrum

18. True or False? Sabine offers the Darksaber to Bo-Katan.

19. Ryder Azadi tells the rebels that what kind of starfighter is being developed by the Empire on Lothal
    a. TIE interceptor
    b. TIE bomber
    c. TIE defender
    d. TIE reaper

20. Who does the Emperor show Ezra inside a rebuilt part of the Jedi Temple to persuade him to open the portal?
    a. Kanan
    b. His parents
    c. Sabine
    d. Yoda

1. What is Zeb's full name?

2. Hera tells Zeb and Ezra they can't return from their shopping trip on Lothal without which item?
   a. A meiloorun fruit
   b. A shield generator
   c. A new droid
   d. A loth-cat

3. What name does Ezra use when he infiltrates the Imperial Academy as a cadet?
   a. Jai Kell
   b. Dev Morgan
   c. Nazhros Oleg
   d. Mart Mattin

4. Ezra's birthday falls on the same day as which other Imperial celebration?

5. Who does Ezra make a deal with to help save Kanan after he is captured by Grand Moff Tarkin?
   a. Hondo Ohnaka
   b. Lando Calrissian
   c. Azmorigan
   d. Cikatro Vizago

6. Which town does Darth Vader order to be burned down to flush out the rebels?

7. Which old friend who could help them find a new base does Ahsoka send the rebels to look for on Seelos?

8. Which bounty hunter used to be in the Imperial Academy with Sabine?
    a. Ketsu Onyo
    b. Dengar
    c. Aurra Sing
    d. Fennec Shand

9. Where does Sabine recommend using as a hyperspace shortcut to Lothal?
    a. Garel
    b. Atollon
    c. Concord Dawn
    d. Ibaar

10. Which of Anakin's qualities does Ahsoka tell Ezra people would have been surprised to know about?
    a. His anger
    b. His kindness
    c. His clumsiness
    d. His sense of humour

11. What is the rebel base on Atollon called?
    a. Chopper Base
    b. Phoenix Base
    c. Echo Base
    d. Phantom Base

12. Who destroys Ezra's first lightsaber?

13. What is the name of the strange being on Atollon, centred between the light and the dark, who trains Kanan?

14. Which Super Tactical Droid from the Clone Wars do the rebels discover is still operational in an abandoned base?
    a. TX-20
    b. TA-175
    c. Kalani
    d. Kraken

15. Sabine picks up the Darksaber on which planet?
    a. Mandalore
    b. Lothal
    c. Dathomir
    d. Seelos

16. The *Ghost* takes on a mission to escort Mon Mothma to a vital meeting on which planet?

17. What colour paint does Sabine use to mark the Imperial transport carrying her father?
    a. Blue
    b. Yellow
    c. Orange
    d. Purple

18. What secret cargo which seems to sing to Ezra do the rebels discover the Empire is shipping from Faos Station?

19. Which animals does Ezra repeatedly see on Lothal which seem to guide him?
    a. Loth-cats
    b. Loth-bats
    c. Loth-wolves
    d. Convors

20. The overseer of the excavation of the Jedi Temple on Lothal tells Sabine the portal is "a pathway between ___".
    a. The past and the future
    b. All time and space
    c. The light and the dark
    d. The Father and the Daughter

1. What is Sabine's callsign among the crew of the *Ghost*?

2. What gift does Sabine give Ezra on Empire Day?

3. What kind of creature does Lando trade Hera for with Azmorigan?

4. What is the name of the engineer Rex knows who is developing a new blockade-busting starfighter?

5. What is Ketsu Onyo's ship called?

6. In which battle does Kanan say that Fenn Rau and his squadron saved his life?

7. Which planet, described in a prophecy as their original homeworld, does Zeb help some Lasat refugees find?

8. What image does Ezra see when he is gazing into the combined Jedi and Sith holocrons?

9. Which two pilots does Sabine help defect from Skystrike Academy?

10. Which family heirloom does Grand Admiral Thrawn steal from Hera's family?

11. Who is the Imperial Viceroy of Mandalore?

12. What are the names of the two people who were also known as Fulcrum?

13. What is Kanan's real name?

14. According to Ezra, what creature always seems to be present at the same time as Ahsoka?

15. Which creatures disappear into hyperspace, taking Grand Admiral Thrawn's Star Destroyer and Ezra with them?

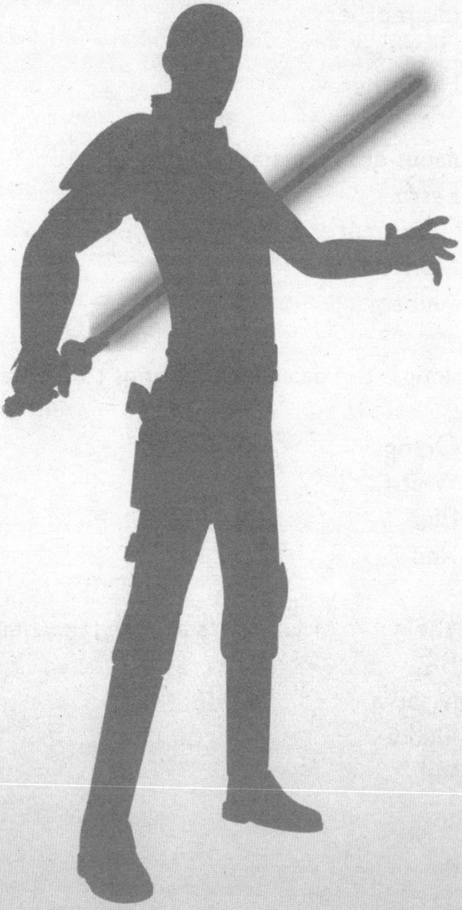

1. What is Cassian's adopted family name?
    a. Tano
    b. Meero
    c. Loy
    d. Andor

2. Who is Cassian looking for on Morlana One?
    a. His brother
    b. His mother
    c. His sister
    d. His father

3. Which planet does Cassian live on?
    a. Ferrix
    b. Coruscant
    c. Morlana One
    d. Aldhani

4. What colour is the droid that belongs to Cassian's mother?
    a. Orange
    b. White
    c. Blue
    d. Red

5. What is the name of Cassian's adopted mother?
    a. Bix
    b. Maarva
    c. Dedra
    d. Vel

6. What's the name of Cassian's friend who works selling scrap technology?
   a. Brasso
   b. Syril
   c. Kassa
   d. Bix

7. Which planet is the capital of the Galactic Empire?
   a. Glee Anselm
   b. Coruscant
   c. Lothal
   d. Corellia

8. What name does Cassian go by while he is doing the Aldhani job?
   a. Clem
   b. Linus
   c. Salman
   d. Verlo

9. After Cassian joins, how many people are in the rebel group on Aldhani?
   a. 5
   b. 6
   c. 7
   d. 8

10. Who does Syril Karn go to live with after being kicked out of his security job?
    a. A friend
    b. His mother
    c. His sister
    d. No one

11. Which senator is a regular visitor to Luthen's gallery?
    a. Bail Organa
    b. Onaconda Farr
    c. Mon Mothma
    d. Padmé Amidala

12. How many TIEs are sent from the nearby airbase once the alarm is raised by the Imperial garrison on Aldhani?
    a. 2
    b. 3
    c. 4
    d. 5

13. According to Syril's boss, "there are no small ____ at the Bureau of Standards."
    a. People
    b. Dreams
    c. Achievements
    d. Jobs

14. What sentence is Cassian given after he is arrested by the Empire?
    a. 2 years
    b. 4 years
    c. 6 years
    d. 8 years

15. What are prisoners told to remove on the transport to Cassian's prison?
    a. Weapons
    b. Boots and shoes
    c. Belts
    d. Hats

16. What order are the prisoners given to make them put their hands on their heads, eyes front and feet on the floor?

17. What colour is the prison uniform Cassian wears?
    a. Blue and white
    b. White and orange
    c. Red and yellow
    d. Black and white

18. Cassian's mother was a past president of a group called The ____ of Ferrix.
    a. Mothers
    b. Sisters
    c. Daughters
    d. Brides

19. Who breaks the water pipe to flood the room during the prison escape?
    a. Kino
    b. Cassian
    c. Melshi
    d. Ulaf

20. What are ashes of important people who die on Ferrix turned into?
    a. Plates
    b. Pots
    c. Bricks
    d. Pictures

1. On which planet does Cassian kill two security guards?

2. What did Cassian's sister call him when they were young?
   a. Kassie
   b. Kasso
   c. Kast
   d. Kassa

3. What piece of tech does Cassian offer Bix's contact?
   a. T-14 hyperdrive
   b. N-S9 Starpath Unit
   c. 473-L transformer
   d. K-spline

4. What planet has Maarva always told everyone Cassian comes from?
   a. Ferrix
   b. Fondor
   c. Fest
   d. Felucia

5. Who is 'the buyer' Bix deals with?

6. Who tells Pre-Mor security that Cassian is on Ferrix?
   a. Bix
   b. Timm
   c. Salman
   d. Brasso

7. Cassian is selling a sealed piece of tech from which Imperial Naval Base?
    a. Steergard
    b. Spellhaus
    c. Fondor
    d. Corellia

8. How old does Cassian say he was when he fought at Mimban?
    a. 14
    b. 15
    c. 16
    d. 17

9. The rebels are trying to steal the quarterly payroll for how large a part of the Empire?

10. In which division of the Empire does Supervisor Meero work?
    a. Imperial Army
    b. Imperial Navy
    c. Imperial Security Bureau
    d. Imperial Bureau of Investigation

11. What kind of crystal does Luthen give Cassian as down payment before the Aldhani job?
    a. Blue sky kyber
    b. Green water kyber
    c. Red fire kyber
    d. Orange earth kyber

12. What natural event do the rebels plan to use as cover to hide their escape from Aldhani?

13. From whom does Syril's mother call in a family favour to get him a job?
    a. Uncle Heff
    b. Uncle Hurst
    c. Uncle Harb
    d. Uncle Harlo

14. What is the call sign of Cassian's team during the Aldhani robbery?
    a. Alpha-One
    b. Bravo-One
    c. Delta-One
    d. Echo-One

15. Which member of the rebel group on Aldhani used to be a stormtrooper?
    a. Taramyn
    b. Cinta
    c. Vel
    d. Skeen

16. What do the Imperials trade with the Dhanis for a 3-year lease of their land?
    a. Nerf meat
    b. Goat hides
    c. Ronto milk
    d. Gundark teeth

17. What does Nemik want Cassian to have after his death?

18. After Cassian is sentenced, to which prison is he sent?
    a. Kessel
    b. Narkina 5
    c. Spellhaus
    d. Segra Milo

19. How much of a loan does Mon Mothma need to cover up her illegal funding of the rebels?

20. Who rescues Supervisor Meera from the mob on Ferrix?

1. From whose scrapyard does Bix transmit messages to her contact?

2. What is the name of Cassian's sister?

3. What was Cassian's first role in the army on Mimban?

4. For how long has the team on Aldhani been preparing before Cassian arrives?

5. What is the name of the concierge who works in Luthen's gallery on Coruscant?

6. What is the sacred valley on Aldhani known as to the native Dhani?

7. How often does the Eye of Aldhani celestial event happen?

8. Which prison does Cassian tell Skeen he was in when he was younger?

9. On which planet is the doctor the rebels take Nemik to after the Aldhani heist?

10. Roughly how many credits does Skeen think they stole from Aldhani?

11. Which prison unit is Cassian assigned to?

12. Who is Cassian's prison unit manager?

13. Who stays with Cassian after the prison break and escapes the planet with him?

14. What fake ID does Luthen transmit to the Imperial cruiser that intercepts him over Segra Milo?

15. What is the name of the undercover ISB agent on Ferrix?

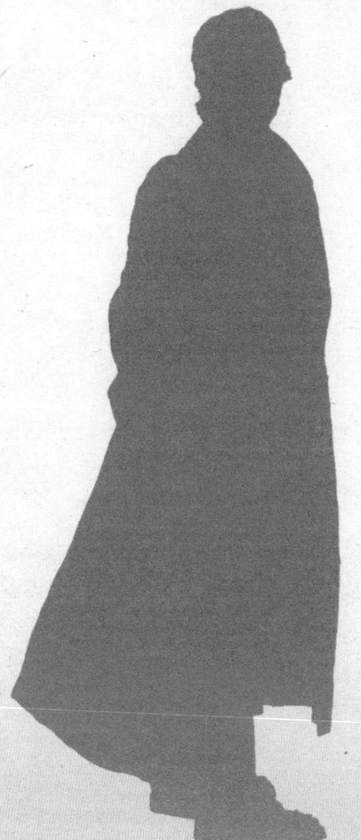

1. What rank does Orson Krennic hold in the Empire?
   a. General
   b. Director
   c. Admiral
   d. Commander

2. What colour armour do death troopers wear?
   a. White
   b. Red
   c. Grey
   d. Black

3. What is the name of Jyn's father?
   a. Anakin
   b. Sheev
   c. Galen
   d. Pao

4. What nickname does Jyn's father give her?
   a. Starlight
   b. Stardust
   c. Starfire
   d. Starshine

5. How many death troopers accompany Krennic when he comes to take Jyn's family away?
   a. 2
   b. 4
   c. 6
   d. 8

6. What does Jyn's mother tell her to trust in?
   a. Herself
   b. The Force
   c. Her friends
   d. Her father

7. What is Jyn's family name?
   a. Calrissian
   b. Erso
   c. Andor
   d. Mothma

8. On which planet is Saw Gerrera's rebel hideout?
   a. Lah'mu
   b. Yavin
   c. Christophsis
   d. Jedha

9. What is the full name of Cassian's robot companion?
   a. R5-D4
   b. C1-10P
   c. FN-2187
   d. K-2SO

10. What is Cassian's rank in the Rebel Alliance?
    a. Sergeant
    b. Lieutenant
    c. Captain
    d. Commander

11. Where does the escaped Imperial pilot hide his message from Jyn's father?
    a. In a pocket
    b. In his boot
    c. Under his hat
    d. In his belt

12. What is the Empire mining on Jedha?
    a. Kyber crystals
    b. Bacta
    c. Tibanna gas
    d. Dedlanite

13. When Saw abandoned her when she was young, he left her with a loaded blaster and what else?
    a. A knife
    b. A comlink
    c. A medpac
    d. A starship

14. On which planet is the facility where Jyn's father works as a scientist developing the Death Star?
    a. Eadu
    b. Corellia
    c. Stygeon Prime
    d. Ithor

15. Who does Krennic go to visit on the volcanic planet of Mustafar?
    a. The Emperor
    b. Grand Moff Tarkin
    c. Galen
    d. Darth Vader

16. According to Cassian and Jyn, what are rebellions built on?
    a. Fear
    b. People
    c. Secrets
    d. Hope

17. Why does K-2 join the rebel group to steal the Death Star plans?
    a. He wants to
    b. He likes Jyn
    c. He doesn't want to be left behind
    d. Cassian says he has to

18. What callsign does Bodhi give the stolen Imperial ship the rebels take to steal the Death Star plans?

19. Complete this saying from Chirrut Îmwe: "I am one with the ____ and the ____ is with me!"
    a. Galaxy
    b. Rebellion
    c. Sky
    d. Force

20. Who activates the master switch so the rebels can talk to the fleet in orbit?
    a. Baze
    b. Cassian
    c. Jyn
    d. Chirrut

1. What is the name of Jyn's mother?
    a. Shmi
    b. Lyra
    c. Qi'ra
    d. Padmé

2. Who does Jyn's mother call for help when Krennic arrives to take them away?
    a. Mon Mothma
    b. Cham Syndulla
    c. Bail Organa
    d. Saw Gerrera

3. Who shoots and wounds Krennic when he comes looking for Jyn's family?
    a. Lyra
    b. Galen
    c. Jyn
    d. A Death Trooper

4. What is the name of the planet where Jyn is being held in an Imperial detention center and labour camp?
    a. Wobani
    b. Lah'mu
    c. Rodia
    d. Devaron

5. What kind of weapon does Cassian's informer, Tivik, tell him the Empire is building?
    a. A new laser
    b. A giant spaceship
    c. A planet killer
    d. An ion bomb

6. What is the full name of the Imperial pilot who Jyn's father sends with the message for Saw Gerrera?

7. What division of the Rebel Alliance does Cassian work in?

8. When questioned by the rebels, how long does Jyn say it has been since she was last in contact with her father?
   a. 5 years
   b. 10 years
   c. 15 years
   d. 20 years

9. What name does Saw give to the creature he uses to read the pilot's mind?

10. On Jedha, who calls K-2 "target practice"?
    a. Cassian
    b. Saw
    c. Baze
    d. Jyn

11. Cassian tells Jyn that Chirrut and Baze are "Guardians of the ____".
    a. Crystals
    b. Light
    c. People
    d. Whills

12. The Temple of the Whills in Jedha City is also known as what?

13. Kyber crystals are used in the construction of the Death Star and which other weapon?

14. Where on Scarif are the technical plans for the Death Star held?

15. Since what age does Cassian say he has been involved in the fight against the Empire?
    a. 6
    b. 8
    c. 10
    d. 16

16. What is the callsign of the stolen Imperial cargo shuttle the rebels use to sneak onto Scarif?
    a. TK-421
    b. SW-0608
    c. YT-1300
    d. ST 321

17. What is the name of the Admiral who leads the rebel fleet's attack on Scarif?
    a. Hera
    b. Ackbar
    c. Vander
    d. Raddus

18. Which rebel squadron is sent through the shield to the surface of Scarif?
    a. Red squadron
    b. Gold squadron
    c. Blue squadron
    d. Green squadron

19. In the attack on Scarif, Cassian tells his group to make 10 men feel like how many?

20. What is the name of the rebel gunner who shoots out the leg of an AT-ST from a U-wing during the Battle of Scarif?
    a. Bistan
    b. Melshi
    c. Dak
    d. Wedge

1. What possession of Jyn's do the death troopers find when looking for her on Lah'mu?

2. How long was Jyn's prison sentence?

3. Where does Cassian meet the informer who tells him about the Empire's new weapon?

4. What does Jyn use to fight her way out of her prison transport?

5. What was the false name Jyn was using when she was rescued by the rebels?

6. What does K-2 say is his specialty?

7. What is the name of the Star Destroyer looming over Jedha city?

8. How old was Jyn when Saw Gerrera left her behind?

9. Which rebel officer orders the attack on Eadu?

10. What kinds of people does Cassian say make up the group who volunteer to go with Jyn to Scarif?

11. How many Star Destroyers are guarding the shield gate over Scarif when Jyn's group arrives?

12. Which landing pad on Scarif are the rebels in the stolen Imperial ship cleared to land on?

13. What is the maximum percentage of their planned path to the Data Vault that K-2 thinks they will complete before they are defeated?

14. Which of these is **not** the secret codename of plans Jyn finds in the Data Vault?
    a. Pax Aurora
    b. Stellarsphere
    c. Darksaber
    d. Stardust

15. What kind of weapon do the rebels use to disable the Star Destroyer over Scarif?

1. Who is C-3PO's droid companion?
    a. BB-8
    b. R2-D2
    c. R5-D4
    d. C1-10P

2. Princess Leia gives R2-D2 plans to which Imperial technology?
    a. TIE fighters
    b. Star Destroyers
    c. The Death Star
    d. Hyperdrives

3. Who does Princess Leia ask for help in her secret message?
    a. Han Solo
    b. Darth Vader
    c. Luke Skywalker
    d. Obi-Wan Kenobi

4. What is Princess Leia's full name?

5. What colour is an Imperial stormtrooper's armour?

6. R2-D2 and C-3PO crash land on which planet?
    a. Tatooine
    b. Dantooine
    c. Dagobah
    d. Coruscant

7. True or False: Luke lives with his parents.

8. What colour is the milk Luke has with his meal on the moisture farm?
    a. White
    b. Red
    c. Green
    d. Blue

9. What is the name of the alien species that finds the droids in the desert?
    a. Rodians
    b. Devaronians
    c. Tuskens
    d. Jawas

10. True or False? Droids are allowed into the Mos Eisley cantina.

11. What colour is Ben Kenobi's lightsaber blade?

12. Who did the lightsaber Ben gives Luke used to belong to?
    a. Luke's father
    b. Luke's mother
    c. Luke's brother
    d. Luke's sister

13. What colour blade is the lightsaber Obi-Wan gives Luke?

14. What is the name of Han Solo's spaceship?

15. How much does Han originally ask Luke and Ben to pay him for a trip to Alderaan?
    a. 5,000 credits
    b. 10,000 credits
    c. 15,000 credits
    d. 20,000 credits

16. True or False? R2-D2 plays a game with Han on board the *Millennium Falcon*.

17. When he first sees it, Luke thinks the Death Star is a small ____?
    a. Planet
    b. Moon
    c. Space Station
    d. Rock

18. What colour is the blade of Darth Vader's lightsaber?

19. Which colour squadron is Luke part of during the attack on the Death Star?
    a. Blue
    b. Gold
    c. Green
    d. Red

20. How many TIE fighters fly alongside Darth Vader as he attacks the rebels in the Death Star trench?
    a. 2
    b. 3
    c. 4
    d. None

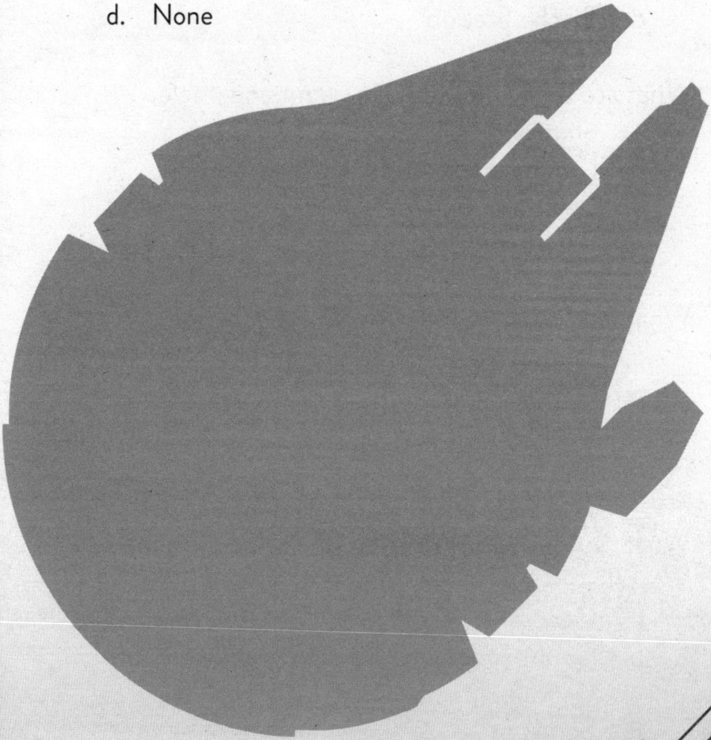

1. What is the name of the diplomatic ship carrying Princess Leia which is captured over Tatooine?
    a. *Tantive IV*
    b. *Raddus*
    c. *Home One*
    d. *Profundity*

2. Where does Luke want to go to pick up some power converters instead of repairing the droids?
    a. Mos Espa
    b. Mos Eisley
    c. Freetown
    d. Tosche Station

3. What are the names of Luke's aunt and uncle?
    a. Shmi and Bail
    b. Luminara and Mace
    c. Daala and Ben
    d. Beru and Owen

4. What kind of animals do Tusken Raiders ride?
    a. Tauntauns
    b. Dewbacks
    c. Banthas
    d. Rancors

5. What rank did Obi-Wan Kenobi have during the Clone Wars?
    a. General
    b. Commander
    c. Captain
    d. Sergeant

6. What is the name of the spaceport where Ben takes Luke?

7. What is the number of the docking bay where Han's ship is parked?

8. What is the name of the crime lord waiting for Han in the docking bay when he returns from the cantina?
    a. Boba Fett
    b. Garindan
    c. Jabba the Hutt
    d. Hondo Ohnaka

9. What does Luke call Han's ship when he first sees it?
    a. A piece of junk
    b. A neat ship
    c. A work of art
    d. A thing of beauty

10. Where does Princess Leia originally tell the Empire the rebel base is located?
    a. Endor
    b. Sullust
    c. Mon Calamari
    d. Dantooine

11. Where on Han's ship do Ben, Luke, Han and Chewbacca hide when it is captured by the Death Star?

12. What is the ID number of the stormtrooper who the Imperial Officer thinks is not at his post guarding Han's ship on the Death Star?

13. What job does Ben undertake on the Death Star so the rebels can escape?
    a. Turns off the tractor beams
    b. Disables the shields
    c. Steal a TIE fighter
    d. Find Princess Leia

14. What do Han, Luke, Leia and Chewbacca escape from the prison level through?

15. Finish the quote from Princess Leia talking about Chewbacca. "Will somebody get this big _____ out of my way!"
    a. Hairy monster
    b. Fluffy alien
    c. Walking carpet
    d. Wet rug

16. What is the name of the moon where the rebel base is located?

17. How wide is the thermal exhaust port of the Death Star which the rebels have to hit with their proton torpedoes?
    a. 1 metre
    b. 2 metres
    c. 5 metres
    d. 10 metres

18. What is the name of Luke's friend from Tatooine who flies with him during the attack on the Death Star?
    a. Dak
    b. Jek
    c. Garven
    d. Biggs

19. How many rebel ships does Darth Vader destroy single-handedly during the Battle of Yavin?
    a. 3
    b. 4
    c. 5
    d. 6

20. Who receives a medal for destroying the Death Star?
    a. Han and Chewbacca
    b. Luke and Leia
    c. Han and Luke
    d. C-3PO and R2-D2

1. What is the name of the Star Destroyer chasing Princess Leia's ship?
    a. *Avenger*
    b. *Executor*
    c. *Devastator*
    d. *Annihilator*

2. Who does C-3PO say he and R2-D2 used to belong to before Luke's uncle bought them?

3. According to Luke, whereabouts on Tatooine does old Ben Kenobi live?

4. What is wrong with the droid which Luke's uncle first buys instead of R2-D2?

5. If they buy a new translator droid, which language does Aunt Beru tell Luke it needs to speak?

6. What is another name for Sand People?

7. What kind of lizard creatures do the stormtroopers ride on Tatooine?

8. What are the names of the aliens who threaten Luke in the cantina?
    a. Greedo and Wuher
    b. Garindan and Momaw Nadon
    c. Muftak and Kabe
    d. Dr Evazan and Ponda Baba

9. What is the name of the band playing in the cantina?

10. How much does Ben promise to pay Han for the trip to Alderaan?

11. What is Tarkin's full name and rank?

12. What kind of creature attacks Luke in the Death Star's trash compactor?

13. What is the level, detention block and cell number where Princess Leia is held on the Death Star?

14. What is the name of the General who organises the rebel assault at the Battle of Yavin?

15. Who are the only two pilots from Red Squadron to survive the attack on the Death Star?

1. What is the name of the planet where the rebels have made their new base?
    a. Chandrila
    b. Kashyyyk
    c. Hoth
    d. Yavin

2. What kind of creatures do the rebels use to ride around in the snow?
    a. Dewbacks
    b. Gundarks
    c. Rancors
    d. Tauntauns

3. Who does Luke see in a vision when he is lost in the snow?
    a. Han Solo
    b. C-3PO
    c. Obi-Wan Kenobi
    d. Yoda

4. To which planet does the person in the vision tell Luke to go?
    a. Naboo
    b. Geonosis
    c. Rodia
    d. Dagobah

5. In the medical room, Leia calls Han a, "scruffy-looking ___".

6. Where does Han fly the *Millennium Falcon* to try and escape from the Star Destroyers over Hoth?
    a. Into an asteroid field
    b. Into a nebula
    c. Into hyperspace
    d. Into a black hole

7. Who goes with Luke to see Yoda?

8. What happens to Luke's X-wing during his training with Yoda?
    a. It tips upside-down
    b. Its wing falls off
    c. It sinks into the swamp
    d. It is attacked by a tree

9. True or False? Yoda is taller than Luke.

10. True or False? Yoda agrees to train Luke as a Jedi straight away.

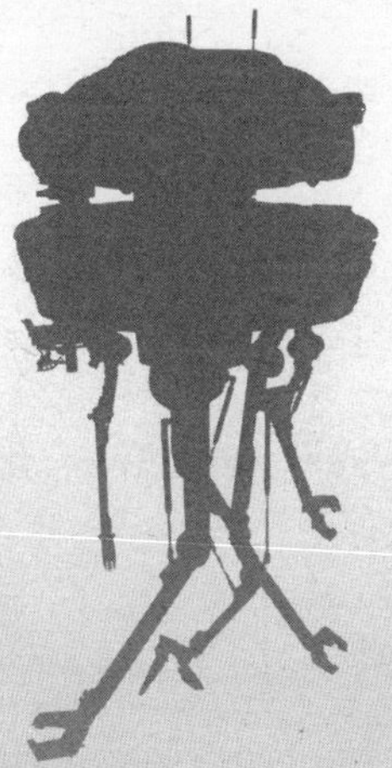

11. Yoda tells Luke: "Adventure. Ha! ____. Ha! A Jedi craves not these things."
    a. Thrills
    b. Action
    c. Excitement
    d. Battles

12. Finish Yoda's piece of advice for Luke: "Do. Or do not. There is no ____"?
    a. Maybe
    b. Try
    c. Failure
    d. Second chance

13. Which bounty hunter follows the *Millennium Falcon* after it escapes from the asteroid field?
    a. Boba Fett
    b. Bossk
    c. IG-88
    d. Zuckuss

14. What is the name of the friend Han thinks can help repair the *Millennium Falcon*?

15. True or False? The friend Han goes to see for repairs behaves in a friendly way when he first sees him.

16. Who tries to repair C-3PO after he is found in pieces?
    a. Han Solo
    b. Princess Leia
    c. Luke Skywalker
    d. Chewbacca

17. Who does Darth Vader want to test the carbon-freezing chamber on before Luke arrives?
    a. Princess Leia
    b. Lando Calrissian
    c. Han Solo
    d. Chewbacca

18. What does Han reply to Leia when she says, "I love you."?
    a. I love you too
    b. Ditto
    c. I feel the same
    d. I know

19. Which of Luke's hands is injured in his battle with Darth Vader?

20. True or False? Obi-Wan Kenobi is Luke's father.

1. On which planet of the Hoth system is the rebel base?
    a. 1st
    b. 3rd
    c. 5th
    d. 6th

2. What is the name the rebels have given their base on Hoth?
    a. Alpha Base
    b. Delta Base
    c. Echo Base
    d. Sierra Base

3. Han calls Leia "your ____," when they are arguing in the corridor of the rebel base?
    a. Magnificence
    b. Highnessness
    c. Worshipfulness
    d. Royalness

4. What is Luke's rank in the Rebellion when he is on Hoth?
    a. Captain
    b. Commander
    c. General
    d. Major

5. What kind of creature attacks Luke when he is out on patrol?
    a. Wampa
    b. Jawa
    c. Rathtar
    d. Krayt dragon

6. Which weapon do the rebels use to disable a Star Destroyer so a transport can escape?
    a. Proton torpedoes
    b. Ion cannon
    c. Blaster cannons
    d. Proton mines

7. What is the name of the Imperial admiral who suffers for bringing the fleet out of hyperspace too close to the rebel base?
    a. Ozzel
    b. Piett
    c. Jerjerrod
    d. Needa

8. What other vehicle besides AT-ATs is seen as part of the Imperial ground assault on the rebel base?

9. Who is in command of Rogue Squadron's rebel snowspeeders?

10. True or False? Luke destroys an Imperial AT-ST with his snowspeeder.

11. What goes wrong with the *Millennium Falcon* when it is trying to escape the Imperial Star Destroyers?
    a. Its communications system breaks down
    b. Its hyperdrive motivator is damaged
    c. Its weapons stop working
    d. It gets a hull breach

12. How many TIE fighters chase the *Millennium Falcon* into the asteroid field?
    a. 3
    b. 4
    c. 5
    d. 6

13. What does Yoda take from Luke's supplies when they first meet?
    a. A blaster
    b. A lamp
    c. Some tools
    d. A helmet

14. Luke calls Dagobah a "slimy ____"?
    a. Swamphole
    b. Mudhole
    c. Waterhole
    d. Sinkhole

15. Who tries to help persuade Yoda to train Luke?

16. What does Yoda accuse Luke of being?
    a. Foolish
    b. Weak
    c. Boring
    d. Reckless

17. Who does Luke seem to meet when he goes into the strange cave on Dagobah?

18. To which planet does Han take the *Millennium Falcon* to get repairs?
    a. Dathomir
    b. Utapau
    c. Kamino
    d. Bespin

19. Which bounty hunter does Darth Vader give Han to after he is frozen in carbonite?

20. True or False? Lando spots Luke hanging from under Cloud City.

1. What is Luke's callsign while riding his tauntaun on Hoth?
2. What is the name of Darth Vader's new Super Star Destroyer flagship?
3. On which planet did Han run into a bounty hunter in the incident which changes his mind about staying with the rebels?
4. After rescuing Luke, Han says he looks strong enough to do what?
5. Where do the Imperial forces land their AT-AT walkers on Hoth?
6. Who is the tailgunner in Luke's speeder during the Battle of Hoth?
7. According to C-3PO, the odds of successfully navigating an asteroid field are approximately what?
8. For how long has Yoda been training Jedi before he meets Luke?
9. What kind of alien creatures attach themselves to the *Millennium Falcon* to feed on the powerlines?
10. On his command ship, how many bounty hunters does Darth Vader talk to about finding the *Millennium Falcon*?

11. What does Darth Vader tell Boba Fett is specifically forbidden in the hunt for the *Millennium Falcon*?

12. Which landing platform on Bespin is the *Millennium Falcon* directed to when it arrives?

13. What is mined at Cloud City on Bespin?

14. What is the name of Lando's cybernetic assistant?

15. In his battle with Luke, what is the only thing Darth Vader says can destroy him?

1. Who does Darth Vader say is coming to personally oversee the completion of the second Death star?
    a. Darth Maul
    b. Grand Moff Tarkin
    c. Admiral Thrawn
    d. The Emperor

2. How many guards stop C-3PO and R2-D2 as they enter Jabba's Palace?
    a. 2
    b. 3
    c. 4
    d. None

3. What gift does Luke give to Jabba?
    a. Money
    b. A blaster
    c. C-3PO and R2-D2
    d. A starship

4. What does the bounty hunter who has captured Chewbacca use to threaten Jabba to pay them more?
    a. A blaster
    b. A lightsaber
    c. A knife
    d. A thermal detonator

5. Who sets Han free from the carbonite?
    a. Luke
    b. Leia
    c. Chewbacca
    d. Lando

6. True or False? Two guards also fall into the pit under Jabba's throne with Luke.

7. What does Luke throw at the lock to bring the gate down on the head of Jabba's pet monster?
   a. A rock
   b. A blaster
   c. A skull
   d. A crate

8. For how long does C-3PO say the rebels will be digested in the belly of the Sarlacc?
   a. 50 years
   b. 100 years
   c. 1,000 years
   d. 10,000 years

9. How many skiffs accompany Jabba's sail barge to the Sarlacc?
   a. 1
   b. 2
   c. 3
   d. 4

10. Who fires his lightsaber over to Luke when he is about to be fed to the Sarlacc?
    a. C-3PO
    b. Leia
    c. Lando
    d. R2-D2

11. What colour is Luke's new lightsaber blade?

12. Who shoots the Sarlacc's tentacle to free Lando?
    a. Luke
    b. Chewbacca
    c. Leia
    d. Han

13. What colour is the uniform of the Emperor's Royal Guard?

14. The second Death Star is being completed in the orbit of which moon?
    a. Sullust
    b. Mandalore
    c. Endor
    d. Ferrix

15. Whose presence does Luke feel on the Super Star Destroyer as the rebel shuttle flies past?
    a. The Emperor
    b. Darth Vader
    c. Admiral Piett
    d. Obi-wan Kenobi

16. What is the name of the Ewok who finds Leia after her speeder bike crashes?
    a. Wicket
    b. Logray
    c. Paploo
    d. Teebo

17. Who sets off the Ewok trap that captures the rebels in a net?
    a. Chewbacca
    b. C-3PO
    c. Leia
    d. R2-D2

18. When they first see him, the Ewoks think C-3PO is some sort of what?
    a. Animal
    b. God
    c. Vehicle
    d. Person

19. What relation exactly is Leia to Luke?
    a. Cousin
    b. Nephew
    c. Sister-in-law
    d. Twin sister

20. What is pulled down by the crowds during the celebrations on Coruscant after the Battle of Endor?
    a. A building
    b. A sign
    c. A statue
    d. An AT-ST walker

1. What does the officer in charge of constructing the second Death Star tell Darth Vader he needs to complete the work?
    a. More time
    b. More men
    c. More money
    d. More materials

2. What is the name of Jabba's majordomo?

3. How much does the bounty hunter demand from Jabba as the bounty for Chewbacca?
    a. 25,000
    b. 30,000
    c. 50,000
    d. 100,000

4. What temporary side-effect of hibernation sickness does Han suffer after he is unfrozen from carbonite?

5. Which Jedi ability does Luke try and use to convince Jabba to release Han?

6. What kind of creature does C-3PO say lives in the pit under Jabba's throne?

7. What does Leia use to defeat Jabba?
    a. Her chains
    b. A blaster
    c. A knife
    d. A lightsaber

8. Which part of C-3PO is damaged by Jabba's jester, Salacious B. Crumb?
    a. Finger
    b. Leg
    c. Eye
    d. Foot

9. Complete the quote from Yoda: "When ____ years old you reach, look as good you will not, hmm?"

10. What is the name of the admiral in command of the rebel fleet during the Battle of Endor?

11. Which of these people isn't in Han's command crew aboard the shuttle?
    a. Lando
    b. Luke
    c. Leia
    d. Chewbacca

12. What does Han tell Chewbacca to do in the shuttle as they are waiting for the Empire to clear them to land on Endor?
    a. Switch the deflector shields
    b. Charge the main guns
    c. Slow down
    d. Fly casual

13. Who is the first rebel to encounter an Ewok?

14. What does Leia first give the Ewok that finds her to try and win them over?

15. How many troops does the Emperor say are waiting in ambush to trap the rebels on Endor?

16. What is Lando's callsign during the Battle of Endor?
    a. Blue Leader
    b. Gold Leader
    c. Red Leader
    d. Green Leader

17. What do the Ewoks use to make an AT-ST fall over as it walks past?

18. How many Imperial fighters follow the rebel ships into the second Death Star?
    a. 1
    b. 2
    c. 6
    d. 10

19. Which part of the *Millennium Falcon* gets damaged as it flies into the second Death Star?
    a. The radar dish
    b. The main guns
    c. The engines
    d. The landing gear

20. Which three Jedi appear to Luke as Force ghosts after Darth Vader's funeral?
    a. Qui-Gon Jinn, Anakin Skywalker and Ahsoka Tano
    b. Obi-Wan Kenobi, Yoda and Mace Windu
    c. Qui-Gon Jinn, Obi-Wan Kenobi and Yoda
    d. Yoda, Anakin Skywalker and Obi-Wan Kenobi

1. What is the name of the Imperial Moff in charge of construction of the second Death Star?

2. What species is Jabba's court jester, Salacious B. Crumb?

3. Where in the Dune Sea does the Sarlacc live?

4. Who is the first person we see become a victim of the rancor?

5. Which bounty hunter does Leia pretend to be when she arrives at Jabba's palace?

6. Who does Mon Mothma say provided the rebels with the information of the second Death Star's location and the Emperor's presence aboard it?

7. What is the name of the Imperial Shuttle which the rebels use to sneak through the Imperial blockade over Endor?

8. What is the name of Lando Calrissian's co-pilot in the *Millennium Falcon* during the Battle of Endor?

9. What does the Emperor refer to Endor as when he tells Darth Vader to go and wait there for Luke?

10. What is the first thing Han tells C-3PO to ask the Ewoks after they become part of the tribe?

11. Leia remembers her mother as being kind but what?

12. Which Ewok steals a speeder bike to distract the guards outside the shield generator bunker?

13. What does Luke say is the Emperor's weakness?

14. Why can't the *Millennium Falcon* get a reading on the second Death Star's shield when the rebels arrive?

15. Which sector does Admiral Ackbar tell Green group to stick close to during the Battle of Endor?

1. From which near-impenetrable material is Mandalorian armour traditionally made?

2. Din Djarin tells the bounty he is hunting on Pagodon, "I can bring you in warm, or I can bring you in ____."
    a. Hot
    b. Cold
    c. Dead
    d. Wet

3. By creed, which piece of armour are Mandalorians not supposed to remove in front of other people?
    a. Their boots
    b. Their helmet
    c. Their pauldron
    d. Their cuirass

4. Who does Din Djarin return his bounties to on Nevarro?
    a. Lando Calrissian
    b. Jabba the Hutt
    c. Cobb Vanth
    d. Greef Karga

5. Who rescues Din Djarin when he is attacked by blurrgs?
    a. Greef Karga
    b. Cad Bane
    c. Chewbacca
    d. Kuiil

6. Which assassin droid was also assigned to capture Grogu?
    a. 4-LOM
    b. IG-88
    c. IG-11
    d. 0-0-0

7. Which alien creatures are stripping Din Djarin's ship for parts when he returns from finding Grogu?
    a. Jawas
    b. Tuskens
    c. Ugnaughts
    d. Niktos

8. What do these creatures finally demand in exchange for returning the ship parts?
    a. The Darksaber
    b. The Rock
    c. The Egg
    d. The Jewel

9. What is the motto of the Way of the Mandalore?

10. Who do Din Djarin and another bounty hunter on Tatooine work together to try and capture?
    a. Migs Mayfield
    b. Fennec Shand
    c. Boba Fett
    d. Xi'an

11. True or False? Din Djarin likes droids.

12. How many X-wings track the New Republic distress beacon to Ranzar Malk's station and destroy it?
    a. 1
    b. 2
    c. 3
    d. 4

13. Who saves Greef Karga's life after a reptavian attack on Nevarro?
    a. Din Djarin
    b. IG-11
    c. Boba Fett
    d. Grogu

14. What is the name of the Imperial Moff who comes looking for Grogu?
    a. Moff Gideon
    b. Moff Tarkin
    c. Moff Jerjerrod
    d. Moff Pryce

15. Who removes Din Djarin's helmet after he is injured in the Imperial siege on Nevarro?
    a. IG-11
    b. Himself
    c. Greef Karga
    d. Grogu

16. What weapon does the Imperial Moff use to cut himself free of his wrecked TIE fighter?
    a. A lightsaber
    b. The Darksaber
    c. A beskar spear
    d. An energy axe

17. True or False? Din Djarin gets swallowed by a krayt dragon.

18. Who tells Din Djarin they can lead him to another Force user?
    a. Bo-Katan Kryze
    b. Kuiil
    c. Morgan Elsbeth
    d. Fennec Shand

19. Which Jedi do they tell him to seek out?
    a. Obi-Wan Kenobi
    b. Kanan Jarrus
    c. Ahsoka Tano
    d. Gungi

20. True or False? The *Razor Crest* gets destroyed on Tython.

1. The Client tells Din Djarin that Grogu is how old?
    a. 10 years old
    b. 25 years old
    c. 50 years old
    d. 100 years old

2. What does IG-11's programming require them to do rather than be captured?

3. What does Din Djarin tell Kuiil are part of his religion?
    a. Helmets
    b. Bounties
    c. Weapons
    d. Foundlings

4. What is Jawa for "The Egg"?

5. Which part of the *Razor Crest*'s controls does Grogu keep stealing?

6. What does Din Djarin give the Tuskens in return for passage across their territory?
    a. A blaster
    b. Some binocs
    c. Some beskar
    d. Some water

7. What does one of the Biker Scouts guarding Grogu think Moff Gideon wants to do with him?
    a. Sell him
    b. Kill him
    c. Eat him
    d. Clone him

8. According to Din Djarin, Mandalorian isn't a race "it's a ____".
    a. Creed
    b. Religion
    c. Belief
    d. Path

9. Din Djarin takes the skull of which creature as his signet?
    a. Krayt dragon
    b. Gundark
    c. Mudhorn
    d. Zillo beat

10. What new piece of equipment does the Armorer give Din Djarin after he escapes from Moff Gideon's trap?
    a. A blaster rifle
    b. A speeder
    c. A jetpack
    d. A helmet

11. When they are under attack from Moff Gideon's TIE fighter, Greef suggests making Grogu "do the ____".

12. What is the name of the Marshal on Tatooine who wears Mandalorian armour?

13. Bo-Katan tells Din Djarin he is a "Child of the ____".
    a. Mythosaur
    b. Force
    c. Watch
    d. Way

14. On which planet does Bo-Katan tell Din Djarin he can find a Jedi?
    a. Corellia
    b. Corvus
    c. Christophsis
    d. Coruscant

15. A garrison of what kind of troops are aboard Moff Gideon's Star Destroyer?

16. Which Jedi arrives to take Grogu into training?
    a. Plo Koon
    b. Kanan Jarrus
    c. Obi-Wan Kenobi
    d. Luke Skywalker

17. How many times does Din Djarin remove his helmet in front of living people?
    a. 1
    b. 2
    c. 3
    d. 4

18. What is Dr. Pershing's designation as a scientist under the New Republic's Amnesty Programme?
    a. M34
    b. L52
    c. G27
    d. G68

19. Moff Gideon is secretly creating clones of which person?
    a. The Emperor
    b. Bo Katan
    c. Himself
    d. Ahsoka Tano

20. Who becomes Marshal of Nevarro after Din Djarin returns from the battle with Moff Gideon on Mandalore?
    a. IG-11
    b. Bo Katan
    c. Ax Woves
    d. Din Djarin

1. According to Kuiil, Din Djarin's Mandalorian ancestors rode which great creature?

2. How many slabs of beskar does Greef Karga get from the successful delivery of Grogu?

3. Where does Greef offer to take Din Djarin to relax after delivering Grogu?

4. On Tatooine, who does Din Djarin agree to help prove himself to the bounty hunter's guild?

5. Which former Imperial sharpshooter runs the crew which breaks Qin out of a New Republic prison ship?

6. What deadly weapon does Moff Gideon have his troopers set up outside the building where Din Djarin is hiding?

7. Who took over the town of Mos Pelgo after the Empire was defeated?

8. What did Cobb Vanth trade with the Jawas for some Mandalorian armour?

9. Peli beats Dr Mandible at sabacc with what hand?

10. Din Djarin discovers that Dr Pershing is performing experiments with what?

11. What information does Ahsoka want to know from the Magistrate of Calodan?

12. What does Boba Fett use to prove the Mandalorian armour is his?

13. What ghastly denizens attack Din Djarin and Bo-Katan in the Mines of Mandalore?

14. Which Jedi was instrumental in helping Grogu escape from the Jedi Temple during Order 66?

15. Which Mandalorian warrior is defeated by Praetorian Guards as he protects the rest of the group so they can escape from Moff Gideon's ambush on Mandalore?

1. Which planet does Boba settle on as the new crime lord?
   a. Dantooine
   b. Jakku
   c. Alderaan
   d. Tatooine

2. Who did the palace Boba takes over originally belong to?
   a. Jabba the Hutt
   b. Dryden Vos
   c. Darth Vader
   d. Saw Gerrera

3. Who is Boba's partner on Tatooine?
   a. Cobb Vanth
   b. Fennec Shand
   c. Cad Bane
   d. Bossk

4. Who steals Boba's armour after he escapes from the Sarlacc?
   a. Tuskens
   b. Pykes
   c. Trandoshans
   d. Jawas

5. Who finds Boba after his escape from the Sarlacc and takes him prisoner?
   a. Stormtroopers
   b. Crimson Dawn
   c. Hutt cartel
   d. Tuskens

6. Boba now expects to receive tributes from the mayor and other criminals in which town?

7. Boba's helmet is mostly which colour?

8. What relation are the Twins to Jabba the Hutt?
    a. Brother and sister
    b. Nephews
    c. Cousins
    d. Son and daughter

9. What vehicles does Boba steal to help the Tuskens stop the train that has been travelling across their territory?
    a. Speeder bikes
    b. Landspeeders
    c. TIE fighters
    d. AT-STs

10. What does the businessman in the Worker's District tell Boba that the Mod gang have been stealing from him?
    a. Food
    b. Water
    c. Weapons
    d. Money

11. According to the Twins, "Tatooine is a worthless ____!"
    a. Planet
    b. Sandpit
    c. Rock
    d. Dump

12. After recovering his ship, what does Boba fly back to the Sarlacc to look for?

13. How long does the Armorer say that Mandalorians have lasted?
    a. 1,000 years
    b. 5,000 years
    c. 10,000 years
    d. 100,000 years

14. Which of the Mandalorian, Din Djarin's possessions does the Armorer melt down to make a gift for Grogu?
    a. His helmet
    b. His cuirass
    c. His spear
    d. His jetpack

15. For what reason does the Armorer exile Din Djarin?
    a. For being a coward
    b. For removing his helmet
    c. For working with the Empire
    d. For stealing

16. How many New Republic X-wings does Din Djarin encounter while testing his new ship over Tatooine?
    a. None
    b. 1
    c. 2
    d. 3

17. Who does Boba's partner hire to help fight the Pykes?
    a. Cad Bane
    b. Bossk
    c. Dengar
    d. Din Djarin

18. What is the name of the club which is blown up by the Pykes?
    a. The Haven
    b. The Sanctuary
    c. The Refuge
    d. The Covert

19. True or False? Boba is faster on the draw than the bounty hunter sent to kill him.

20. After the battle in the town, who manages to calm the rampaging rancor?
    a. Fennec Shand
    b. Grogu
    c. Boba Fett
    d. Cobb Vanth

1. Boba is referred to by what title after he takes over Bib Fortuna's territory in Mos Espa?

2. Boba says that Jabba ruled with fear. What does Boba intend to rule with?
    a. Power
    b. Money
    c. Respect
    d. Understanding

3. How many assassins attack Fennec and Boba after their first visit to Mos Espa?
    a. 3
    b. 4
    c. 5
    d. 6

4. What is the name of the Wookiee working with the Twins?

5. What is the train running across the Tusken territory of the Dune Sea carrying?
    a. Spice
    b. Money
    c. Coaxium
    d. Weapons

6. After Jabba's death, Mos Espa was divided up between how many families?
   a. 2
   b. 3
   c. 4
   d. 5

7. What do the Twins offer Boba as an apology for trying to kill him?

8. Which group of people does the rancor keeper say is said to have learned to ride rancors?

9. What does Boba ask Fennec to help him recover in return for saving her life on Tatooine?

10. What does Boba say he can offer Fennec that no client ever has?
    a. Freedom
    b. Loyalty
    c. Respect
    d. Peace

11. Which part of himself does Din Djarin injure with the Darksaber?
    a. His arm
    b. His leg
    c. His hand
    d. His foot

12. What does Din Djarin find in the lower substrata of Glavis Ringworld?

13. The incident when the Empire destroyed Mandalore is known to Mandalorians as the "Night of ___".
    a. A Hundred Shadows
    b. A Thousand Flames
    c. A Thousand Tears
    d. A Hundred Sorrows

14. In the covert, who challenges Din Djarin for the Darksaber?
    a. The Armorer
    b. Paz Vizsla
    c. Pre Vizsla
    d. Bo-Katan

15. According to Creed, a Mandalorian can only be redeemed in the living waters beneath the mines of which planet?

16. True or False? Din Djarin gets to spend time with Grogu while he is being trained by Luke.

17. Which bounty hunter guns down Cobb Vanth?
    a. IG-88
    b. Bossk
    c. Zuckuss
    d. Cad Bane

18. What does the town of Mos Pelgo change its name to?

19. What is the gift which the Armorer makes for Grogu?

20. Who does Cad Bane tell Boba was responsible for killing his Tusken tribe?
    a. Crimson Dawn
    b. Pyke Syndicate
    c. Hutts
    d. Stormtroopers

1. Boba cuts his bonds on the teeth of which creature to try and escape the Tuskens?
2. Which Trandoshan is the protector of the city center and businesses of Mos Eisley?
3. Who is the mayor of Mos Espa?
4. What is the name of the person who owns the Sanctuary?
5. Which order of assassins attack Fennec and Boba on the streets of Mos Espa?
6. What did Krrsantan used to be before becoming a bounty hunter?
7. How many credits do the street Mod gang owe the water vendor?
8. The Pykes tell Boba that which other group has already collected protection money from them?
9. Where does Boba take Fennec to save her life after finding her body?
10. Krrsantan starts a fight with a group of which species in the Sanctuary?
11. Who is the leader of the band that plays at the Sanctuary?

12. Where is Din Djarin told he can find an entrance to the lower substrata of Glavis Ringworld?

13. The Pykes hide a bomb in the Sanctuary, concealed inside what object?

14. Whose lightsaber does Luke offer to Grogu?

15. Who flies Grogu to Tatooine after he chooses to end his training?

1. Who gives Kaz his mission as a spy for the Resistance?
    a. Leia
    b. Han
    c. Rey
    d. Poe

2. What is Kaz's full name?

3. To which planet is Kaz first sent as a spy to gather information on the First Order?
    a. Dantooine
    b. Castilon
    c. D'Qar
    d. Takodana

4. What is the name of the refuelling platform which Kaz is asked to spy on?
    a. *Giant*
    b. *Monster*
    c. *Colossus*
    d. *Enormity*

5. What colour jacket does Kaz usually wear?
    a. Yellow
    b. Red
    c. Blue
    d. Green

6. What is the name of the ship Yeager lets Kaz use for his first race?
    a. *Fireball*
    b. *Firestorm*
    c. *Firelight*
    d. *Firefly*

7. What are the names of the aliens who run the Office of Acquisitions?
    a. Bix and Neeku
    b. Flix and Reva
    c. Tam and Yeager
    d. Flix and Orka

8. True or False? Kaz wins his first race.

9. Who is giving the orders to the pirate gang that keeps attacking the platform?
    a. Kylo Ren
    b. General Hux
    c. Captain Phasma
    d. Supreme Leader Snoke

10. What colour armour does Commander Pyre wear?
    a. Silver
    b. White
    c. Gold
    d. Black

11. Who do Poe and Kaz rescue, thinking they are a survivor of a pirate attack?
    a. Synara
    b. Torra
    c. Gorrak
    d. Kragan

12. What shape is on the face masks of the Guavian Death Gang?
    a. Star
    b. Square
    c. Triangle
    d. Circle

13. How may legs does Torra's pet have?
    a. 2
    b. 4
    c. 6
    d. 8

14. What does Neeku discover the platform has when he's in the control centre during the First Order's attempt to take it over?
    a. A hyperdrive
    b. Shields
    c. Turbolasers
    d. Wheels

15. Who destroys the red First Order starfighter in the battle for the station?
    a. Poe
    b. Kaz
    c. Torra
    d. Yeager

16. True or False? Kaz's father and family survived the First Order attack on their homeworld.

17. What nickname does Hype give Kaz when he first joins the Aces?
    a. Kazdoom
    b. Kaztastrophe
    c. Kazloser
    d. Kazzie

18. What does Flix think is hidden beneath the surface of his home planet?
    a. Rancors
    b. Gundarks
    c. Dragons
    d. Wampas

19. Which high-ranking First Order officer does Kaz help find his way on the *Titan* refuelling station?
    a. Captain Phasma
    b. Commander Pyre
    c. General Hux
    d. Allegiant General Pryde

20. What does Yeager give Kaz when he leaves to join the Resistance?
    a. A book
    b. A trophy
    c. The *Fireball*
    d. A droid

1. What is Kaz's father's profession?
    a. Spy
    b. Senator
    c. Soldier
    d. Sky racer

2. Who wins the first sky race Kaz watches on the *Colossus*?

3. What is the name of the pilot of the red First Order starfighter?
    a. Captain Phasma
    b. Commander Pyre
    c. Major Vonreg
    d. Lieutenant Mitaka

4. Where does Kaz tell Tam he trained as a mechanic in a ship factory?
    a. Coruscant
    b. Corellia
    c. Fondor
    d. Jakku

5. What is the nickname Tam has for hyperfuel?
    a. Hot stuff
    b. Hot fire
    c. Hot sauce
    d. Hot lightning

6. How much is the reward for the runaway children that Kaz goes looking for?
   a. 10,000 credits
   b. 15,000 credits
   c. 20,000 credits
   d. 25,000 credits

7. What are the names of the two runaway children?

8. Who does Marcus Speedstar owe 20,000 credits?
   a. Hutt Cartel
   b. Guavian Death Gang
   c. Kanjiklub
   d. Crimson Dawn

9. What is the name of Torra's pet voorpak?
   a. Buggles
   b. Biggles
   c. Boggles
   d. Boogles

10. What does Kaz find in the wardrobe in Doza's office?

11. What does Kaz use as a code name for Poe?
    a. Dark Wolf
    b. White Wolf
    c. Star Wolf
    d. Lone Wolf

12. Which system do Kaz and Tam watch being destroyed by Starkiller Base?
    a. D'Qar
    b. Hosnian Prime
    c. Takodana
    d. Batuu

13. How long has it been since the *Colossus* moved?
    a. 10 years
    b. 20 years
    c. 25 years
    d. 30 years

14. What is the name of Tam's First Order pilot trainer?
    a. Lieutenant Galek
    b. Lieutenant Mitaka
    c. Lieutenant Greel
    d. Lieutenant San

15. What strange building does Kaz get trapped in on the trading outpost of Ashas Ree?

16. What sort of business does Hype's friend Vranki run?

17. What is the name of the First Order refuelling station which is the same type as the *Colossus*?

18. Which bounty hunter in the Varkana system is paid by the First Order to find Resistance spies?
    a. Dengar
    b. 4-LOM
    c. Aurra Sing
    d. Ax Tagrin

19. What is the name of the new world the *Colossus* finds in the Outer Rim which could be a possible safe haven?
    a. Aeos Prime
    b. Tehar
    c. Drahgor III
    d. Vanqor

20. Which part of the First Order destroyer do Jade Squadron and the Aces target in the final battle in the Barabesh system?

1. What does Kaz call the droid that flies with him when he is a New Republic pilot?

2. Who does Kaz lose 1,500 credits to playing darts?

3. What does Aunt Z say are the odds of Kaz winning his first race?

4. Whose logo does Kaz agree to put on his racer in the first race?

5. What is Kaz's lucky trophy made from?

6. What are the names of all the pilots in Ace squadron before Kaz joins the group?

7. What starship trick does Poe show Kaz as they're flying through an asteroid field?

8. Kaz joins Poe on a reconnaissance mission to which First Order outpost?

9. What do Poe and Kaz discover the First Order have been mining in huge quantities?

10. How far from D'Qar is the *Colossus* after its jump from Castilon?

11. What is Tam's First Order cadet pilot number?

12. Which Ace Squadron pilot used to be in the Empire?

13. What career does Flanx say Flix once wanted to pursue?

14. Which pirate puts a 'curse' on Kaz after losing to him at gambling?

15. Who does Kragan buy battle droids from to help the pirates try to take over the *Colossus*?

1. Who has vanished?
    a. Leia
    b. Luke
    c. Han
    d. C-3PO

2. What is the name of the evil power that has risen from the ashes of the Galactic Empire?

3. To which planet have the Resistance sent a pilot on a secret mission?
    a. Takodana
    b. D'Qar
    c. Hosnian Prime
    d. Jakku

4. What is the name of the pilot sent on the secret mission?

5. What colours are BB-8?
    a. White and red
    b. White and blue
    c. White and orange
    d. White and green

6. True or False? The scavenger girl trades BB-8 for food.

7. What vehicle do Poe and the stormtrooper steal to escape the First Order ship?

8. What does Poe call the stormtrooper who helps him escape from the First Order?
   a. Fred
   b. Frank
   c. Finn
   d. Fong

9. Which group does the scavenger girl think the escaped stormtrooper is with when they first meet?
   a. The First Order
   b. The Rebellion
   c. Crimson Dawn
   d. The Resistance

10. What is the name of the scavenger girl who helps the escaped stormtrooper flee from the planet after he crashes?
    a. Rose
    b. Rey
    c. Raya
    d. Rita

11. When they finally return to the *Millennium Falcon*, Han tells Chewbacca, "Chewie, we're ____!"
    a. Back
    b. Lost
    c. Home
    d. Free

12. Who accidentally sets the creatures free on Han and Chewbacca's freighter?
    a. Finn
    b. Chewbacca
    c. Han
    d. Rey

13. What is the name of the First Order's new superweapon?
    a. Starkiller Base
    b. Sunkiller Base
    c. Starstriker Base
    d. Sunstriker Base

14. What is the name of the First Order's Supreme Leader?
    a. Hux
    b. Snoke
    c. Bix
    d. Snap

15. What does Rey find in the rooms beneath the castle on Takodana?
    a. A blaster
    b. A lightsaber
    c. A droid
    d. A speeder

16. Who captures Rey on Takodana?

17. Which powered-down droid does BB-8 uncover in the Resistance base?
    a. C-3PO
    b. R5-D4
    c. R4-P17
    d. R2-D2

18. What is Poe's callsign during the attack on the First Order base?
    a. Black One
    b. Black Leader
    c. Rogue Leader
    d. Red One

19. Who shoots Kylo after he defeats Han Solo?
    a. Rey
    b. Finn
    c. Chewbacca
    d. Leia

20. True or False? Chewbacca and R2-D2 accompany Rey to the planet where Luke Skywalker is hiding.

1. Who leads the stormtroopers on Jakku?

2. How many bloody finger streaks are left across the helmet of a First Order stormtrooper during the attack on the village on Jakku?

3. To whom does Rey sell her salvaged parts?
   a. Lor San Tekka
   b. Unkar Plutt
   c. Bala-Tik
   d. Teedo

4. Which part of BB-8 does Rey fix when she first meets him?
   a. Motivator
   b. Selenium drive
   c. Tooling disc
   d. Antenna

5. How many cannons on the First Order ship do Poe and Finn destroy during their escape?
   a. 1
   b. 2
   c. 3
   d. 4

6. What does Finn find in the wreckage of their ship after it crashes on Jakku?

7. What creature is also drinking water from the trough along with Finn?
    a. Happabore
    b. Teedo
    c. Steelpecker
    d. Luggabeast

8. What kind of ship does Rey first plan on using to escape from Jakku with Finn?
    a. X-wing
    b. Corellian YT freighter
    c. Quadjumper
    d. T-16 skyhopper

9. What does Rey tell Finn the *Millennium Falcon* is as they run past?

10. On which planet is the Resistance base?
    a. Takodana
    b. Malastare
    c. Eriadu
    d. D'Qar

11. Rey tells Han she thinks the *Millennium Falcon* made the Kessel run in how many parsecs?

12. What kind of creatures are being transported on Han and Chewbacca's freighter?
    a. Tauntauns
    b. Rancors
    c. Rathtars
    d. Gundarks

13. How many times does Finn tell Han Chewbacca has nearly killed him when he is looking after him?
    a. 2
    b. 5
    c. 6
    d. 10

14. What does Han refer to BB-8 as when he walks past him on the *Millennium Falcon*?
    a. Bucket
    b. Scrap
    c. Ball
    d. Droid

15. Who does Han take Rey and Finn to see on Takodana?

16. Who does Han's contact refer to as her boyfriend?
    a. Han
    b. Finn
    c. Luke
    d. Chewbacca

17. Who is the first person to use the lightsaber Rey finds?
    a. Rey
    b. Finn
    c. Han
    d. Poe

18. What is Finn called by a stormtrooper at the battle on Takodana?

19. Han tells Leia he thinks there's too much of whom in Kylo?

20. Who do Finn, Han and Chewbacca capture and force to lower the shields on Starkiller Base?

1. Who is the old ally on Jakku who has part of the map to Luke's location?

2. What does Captain Phasma ask FN-2187 to submit for inspection after the attack on the village?

3. Where does Rey go to sell her salvage?

4. On Jakku, Rey lives in the wreck of what kind of vehicle?
5. Rey tells BB-8 to stay away from which two areas on the way back to the outpost?
6. How much food is Rey offered for BB-8?
7. Why do Han and Rey think having a compressor on the ignition line of the *Millennium Falcon* is a mistake?
8. For whom is Han transporting the rathtars?
9. Which two groups are chasing Han to repay the money they loaned him?
10. How much money did Han borrow from each group?
11. What was the name of the capital of the New Republic which was destroyed by Starkiller Base?
12. Which Resistance pilot flew the reconnaissance mission over Starkiller Base?
13. Which other veteran of the Battle of Endor is also part of the attack on Starkiller Base?
14. According to Finn, in which precinct of Starkiller Base is the crucial thermal oscillator located?
15. How many Resistance X-wings survive the attack on Starkiller Base?

1. Who leads the First Order's attack on the Resistance as they try to flee from their base?
    a. General Hux
    b. Supreme Leader Snoke
    c. Captain Kagi
    d. Captain Phasma

2. True or False? Leia orders Poe to continue his attack on the First Order dreadnought rather than retreat.

3. How many Resistance bombers drop their bombs on the First Order dreadnought
    a. 0
    b. 1
    c. 2
    d. 3

4. What does Luke do with the lightsaber Rey gives him?
    a. Puts it in his pocket
    b. Throws it away
    c. Gives it back
    d. Takes it apart

5. Who knocks the door to Luke's home off its hinges?
    a. Rey
    b. Luke
    c. Chewbacca
    d. R2-D2

6. What remains in the galaxy as long as Luke lives, according to Supreme Leader Snoke?
   a. Light
   b. Hope
   c. Peace
   d. Balance

7. Why did Luke tell Rey he went to the island on Ahch-To?
   a. To sleep
   b. To hide
   c. To mourn
   d. To die

8. Who picks up Leia's homing beacon after she is injured?
   a. Poe
   b. C-3PO
   c. Finn
   d. Lieutenant Connix

9. How many lessons does Luke finally agree to give Rey?
   a. 1
   b. 2
   c. 3
   d. 4

10. Who stops Finn from taking an escape pod to go and find Rey?
   a. Rose
   b. Leia
   c. Poe
   d. C-3PO

11. What does Rey do when she first sees Kylo through their Force connection?
    a. Holds his hand
    b. Blasts him
    c. Takes his lightsaber
    d. Throws a rock at him

12. What does Rey accidentally cut in half when practising with a lightsaber?
    a. A tree
    b. A rock
    c. A table
    d. A door

13. Who disables the guards so Rose and Finn can escape from their prison?
    a. Finn
    b. Rose
    c. BB-8
    d. R2-D2

14. True or false? Kylo and Rey are able to touch each other through their Force connection.

15. What colour is the blade of Ben Solo's lightsaber?

16. Who appears to Luke as a Force ghost when he tries to burn down the sacred tree?
    a. Obi-wan Kenobi
    b. Anakin Skywalker
    c. Yoda
    d. Qui-Gon Jinn

17. What colour robes does Supreme Leader Snoke wear?
    a. Black
    b. Gold
    c. Red
    d. White

18. Who says they were the one who created the Force connection between Rey and Kylo?
    a. Luke
    b. Kylo
    c. Snoke
    d. Yoda

19. When they are trying to escape from Supreme Leader Snoke's ship, who tries to stop Rose and Finn from reaching the shuttle?
    a. General Hux
    b. Captain Phasma
    c. Captain Canady
    d. Commander Trach

20. Under the white mineral covering, what colour is the surface of the planet where the remainder of the Resistance make a stand against the First Order?
    a. Green
    b. Red
    c. Blue
    d. Yellow

1. What is disabled on Poe's fighter when he is attacking the First Order dreadnought to cover the Resistance as they escape?
    a. Shields
    b. Engines
    c. Weapons systems
    d. Landing gear

2. Which Resistance bomber crew member finally triggers the release of the bombs?
    a. Paige
    b. Nix
    c. Rose
    d. Edon

3. What is the name of bird-like creatures that live on the island with Luke?
    a. Moofs
    b. Porgs
    c. Gundarks
    d. Mynocks

4. What is Finn's first word when he wakes up in his med pod?

5. What does Rey spot hidden in the sea off the coast of the island where Luke is hiding?
    a. A Star Destroyer
    b. A TIE fighter
    c. An X-wing
    d. A B-wing

6. Snoke tells Kylo that he is no Darth Vader, "just a child in a ____".
   a. Cape
   b. Mask
   c. Helmet
   d. Dream

7. What does R2-D2 show Luke to change his mind about helping Rey?

8. Who takes over command of the Resistance fleet after Leia is injured?
   a. Admiral Ackbar
   b. Vice Admiral Holdo
   c. General Rieekan
   d. Admiral Statura

9. Who does Poe call for help in getting through First Order security?
   a. Lando
   b. Maz
   c. Chewbacca
   d. Luke

10. Where are Rose and Finn told they can find a master codebreaker to help with their plans to disable the First Order's active tracking?

11. Rose and Finn watch a race involving what kind of creatures?
    a. Fathiers
    b. Veractyls
    c. Dewbacks
    d. Tauntauns

12. How many students did Luke say he took when he started his training temple?
    a. 12
    b. 13
    c. 14
    d. 15

13. When Rey enters the mirror cave under the island, who does she see instead of her parents?

14. According to Yoda, what is the greatest teacher?
    a. The Force
    b. Failure
    c. Practice
    d. Patience

15. What do Rose and Finn use to disguise BB-8 when they sneak aboard Supreme Leader Snoke's ship?

16. Who stays behind to pilot the Resistance cruiser so the transports can escape?

17. Who did Supreme Leader Snoke wrongly think was Kylo's equal on the light side?

18. Where does Kylo tell Rey her parents are?
    a. Jakku
    b. Coruscant
    c. Exegol
    d. Mustafar

19. What mineral covers much of the surface of the planet Crait?

20. What does Luke give Leia before he leaves to face Kylo at the Battle of Crait?

1. How many of the First Order dreadnought's surface cannons are left for Poe to destroy when it finally launches its fighters?

2. What does Poe think BB-8 is saying when he sees Finn after he comes out of his med pod?

3. What creature does Rey see Luke milking?

4. For how long does Rose say the First Order will be unaware their tracker is disabled if they are successful?

5. When Rose and Finn leave on their mission, how much fuel does the Resistance fleet have left?

6. What are Rose and Finn told the master codebreaker will be wearing on their lapel?

7. What is the name of the alien who tells Rose and Finn they can't leave their shuttle on the beach at Canto Bight?

8. What does DJ put around his neck when Rose and Finn meet him in their cell?

9. What is Rose's medallion made from?

10. Which First Order droid becomes suspicious of Rose, Finn, DJ and BB-8?

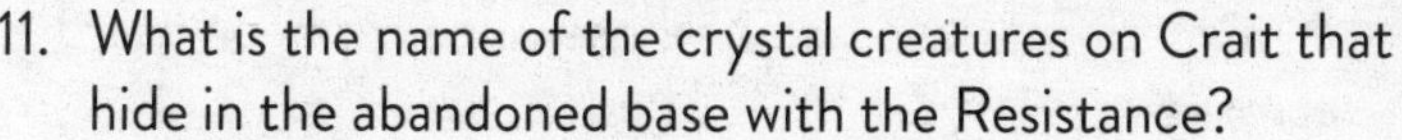

11. What is the name of the crystal creatures on Crait that hide in the abandoned base with the Resistance?

12. The battering-ram cannon used at the Battle of Crait incorporates miniaturised technology from which other weapon?

13. What does Finn forget to engage on his skim speeder until Rose tells him?

14. How many ski speeders are sent out to face the First Order at the Battle of Crait?

15. According to C-3PO, what are the odds of finding an exit from the mine on Crait?

1. A mysterious broadcast in whose voice has been heard across the galaxy?
   a. Darth Vader
   b. Kylo Ren
   c. Luke Skywalker
   d. Emperor Palpatine

2. Finn uploads the message from the Resistance's new spy in the First Order to which droid?
   a. BB-8
   b. C-3PO
   c. R2-D2
   d. R5-D4

3. Who does Rey tell Leia had already nearly found the location of Exegol?
   a. Han Solo
   b. Luke Skywalker
   c. Lando Calrissian
   d. Chewbacca

4. According to C-3PO, the festival on Pasaana is known for its "Colourful ___ and delectable sweets".
   a. Clothes
   b. Tents
   c. Kites
   d. Vehicles

5. What does Kylo snatch from Rey during their Force connection when she is on Pasaana?
   a. Her lightsaber
   b. Her blaster
   c. Her bag
   d. Her necklace

6. Who hotwires the speeders so Rey and the rest of the team can flee the festival from the First Order?
   a. Poe
   b. BB-8
   c. Chewbacca
   d. C-3PO

7. What do some of the First Order troopers chasing Rey and her friends on Pasaana do, which is a surprise?
   a. Use the Force
   b. Fly
   c. Surrender
   d. Run away

8. Which runic language does C-3PO say is written on the dagger BB-8 finds?
   a. Huttese
   b. Sith
   c. Kaminoan
   d. Geonosian

9. Who gets captured on Pasaana by the First Order and the Knights of Ren?
   a. Lando
   b. Finn
   c. Poe
   d. Chewbacca

10. Which hip does Rey wear her lightsaber on?

11. Zorii tells Poe that the First Order win by "making you think you're ____".
    a. Alone
    b. Already dead
    c. Weak
    d. Unimportant

12. True or False? BB-8 goes with Finn, Rey and Poe on the rescue mission to Kylo Ren's Star Destroyer.

13. Who do Poe, Chewbacca and Finn find out is the secret spy in the First Order?
    a. Kylo Ren
    b. General Hux
    c. Captain Phasma
    d. Allegiant General Pryde

14. What relation is Rey to Emperor Palpatine?
    a. Sister
    b. Daughter
    c. Granddaughter
    d. Great granddaughter

15. Who appears to Kylo after his battle with Rey on the wreckage of the Death Star?
    a. Luke
    b. Leia
    c. Han
    d. Anakin

16. Who restores C-3PO's memory?
    a. R2-D2
    b. Maz Kanata
    c. Leia
    d. Chewbacca

17. Who goes to the Core systems to send a message for people to come and help the Resistance at Exegol?
    a. Rey and BB-8
    b. C-3PO and R2-D2
    c. Lando and Chewbacca
    d. Finn and Rose

18. What colour armour do Sith troopers wear?
    a. White
    b. Black
    c. Silver
    d. Red

19. What colour is the blade of the lightsaber Rey makes for herself?
    a. Red
    b. Blue
    c. Green
    d. Yellow

20. What does Rey tell the person outside the Lars homestead on Tatooine is her surname?
    a. Solo
    b. Antilles
    c. Skywalker
    d. Calrissian

1. On which Planet does Kylo find Palpatine?
    a. Ferrix
    b. Castilon
    c. Exegol
    d. Hosnian Prime

2. What does Palpatine reveal to Kylo that was hidden in the planet?
    a. An army of soldiers
    b. A fleet of Star Destroyers
    c. A new lightsaber
    d. Ancient Sith books

3. What does Palpatine call this hidden gift for Kylo?
    a. The Last Order
    b. The Final Order
    c. The Ultimate Order
    d. The Hidden Order

4. What does Leia tell Rey to never underestimate?
    a. The Sith
    b. The First Order
    c. The Resistance
    d. A droid

5. What is the name of the group of fearsome warriors who enforce Kylo's will?

6. What does the alien on Pasaana who gives Rey a necklace want to know about her?
    a. Her family name
    b. Where she comes from
    c. Who her friends are
    d. Why she is there

7. According to Lando, how many Sith wayfinders were made?

8. What does BB-8 use to distract the First Order troopers chasing their speeders?
    a. Rocks
    b. Bags
    c. Rope
    d. Coloured smoke

9. What do BB-8 and Rey find near Ochi's bones?

10. Rey uses her lightsaber to slice off the wing from which side of Kylo's ship?

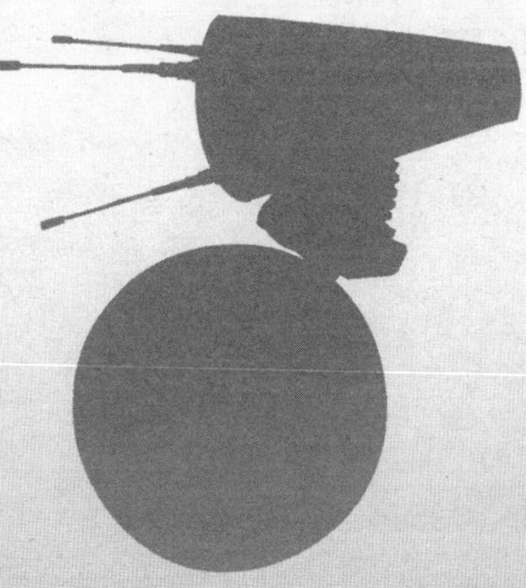

11. In her vision, Rey tells Finn she saw Kylo and who else sitting on the Sith throne?
    a. Vader
    b. Palpatine
    c. Luke
    d. Herself

12. What is the name of the droid BB-8 finds on Ochi's ship?

13. What does Zorii reveal that Poe used to do as a job?
    a. Scrap dealer
    b. Pod racer
    c. Spice runner
    d. Gambler

14. The dagger inscription reveals the location of Palpatine's Sith wayfinder is on a moon in which system?

15. What does Kylo see in his Force connection with Rey on Kijimi that reveals where she is hiding?
    a. Her lightsaber
    b. A computer terminal
    c. Vader's helmet
    d. A TIE fighter

16. Kylo tells Rey that they are a "____ in the Force".
    a. Union
    b. Dyad
    c. Schism
    d. Flaw

17. Who leads the group that offers to take Rey and her friends across the water to the wreck of the second Death Star?
    a. Jannah
    b. Zorii
    c. Bix
    d. Q'ira

18. Where does Rey flee to after defeating Kylo in battle?
    a. Jakku
    b. Ahch-To
    c. Kenari
    d. Glee Anselm

19. What kind of ship does Kylo use to travel to Exegol after his battle with Rey?

20. What does Rey bury in the sand outside the Lars homestead on Tatooine?

1. In the Sinta Glacier Colony, who passes Finn the message for Leia from the new spy in the First Order?

2. On which planet is the new Resistance base where Rey continues her training?

3. Poe blows which parts of the *Millennium Falcon* when lightspeed skipping to escape the First Order?

4. What celebration is happening on Pasaana when Rey arrives?

5. Who were Luke and Lando following when they came to Pasaana looking for a Sith wayfinder?

6. What kind of creature does Rey heal in the tunnels under the desert of Pasaana?

7. Where does Finn think they'll all be thrown if the First Order catches them?

8. To which planet does Poe lead them to find a droidsmith to access C-3PO's memory?

9. Where does Zorii tell Poe she is planning to escape to?

10. According to the dagger's inscription, what are the exact coordinates of the location of the Emperor's Sith wayfinder?

11. The wreckage of the second Death Star where the Emperor's Sith wayfinder is hidden is on which moon?

12. What is Jannah's former First Order trooper ID?

13. Who is the gunner aboard the *Millennium Falcon* during the Battle of Exegol?

14. What does Maz give Chewbacca after the Battle of Exegol?

15. From which system does Lando tell Jannah he is from?

SECTION TWO:

THE GALAXY

1. The N-1 starfighters used at the Battle of Naboo are mostly which colour?
    a. Blue
    b. Red
    c. Yellow
    d. Green

2. What vehicle does Anakin use in a surprising way to attack General Grievous' ship in the asteroids of the Bothawui system?
    a. Landspeeders
    b. Escape pods
    c. AT-TE walkers
    d. Skimmers

3. What colour is the *Millennium Falcon* when it belongs to Lando Calrissian?
    a. Red and white
    b. White and blue
    c. Yellow and white
    d. Green and white

4. What is the name of Hera Syndulla's starship which is used as a base by a small group of rebels?
    a. *Phantom*
    b. *Spectre*
    c. *Shadow*
    d. *Ghost*

5. What kind of vehicle do Jawas often travel in?
    a. AT-AT
    b. AT-ST
    c. Landspeeder
    d. Sandcrawler

6. How many engines does Luke's landspeeder have?
    a. 1
    b. 2
    c. 3
    d. 4

7. What kind of ships fire on the *Millennium Falcon* as it leaves Tatooine on the way to Alderaan?
    a. Y-wings
    b. Star Destroyers
    c. TIE fighters
    d. Gozanti cruisers

8. What is the squadron colour of the Y-wings at the Battle of Yavin?
    a. Red
    b. Blue
    c. Green
    d. Gold

9. What kind of ships do the Empire send to fight the rebel starfighters attacking the first Death Star?
    a. Star Destroyers
    b. TIE fighters
    c. TIE bombers
    d. B-wings

10. AT-AT walker stands for “All Terrain ____ Transport walker”.
    a. Artificial
    b. Armoured
    c. Army
    d. Automated

11. How many legs does an AT-AT walker have?
    a. 2
    b. 4
    c. 6
    d. 8

12. What kind of ship does Luke fly to Dagobah?
    a. A-wing
    b. B-wing
    c. X-wing
    d. Y-wing

13. What kind of rebel starfighter crashes into the bridge of a Super Star Destroyer at the Battle of Endor?
    a. A-wing
    b. U-wing
    c. X-wing
    d. Y-wing

14. How many domed shield generators are there on the command tower of an Imperial Star Destroyer?
    a. 1
    b. 2
    c. 3
    d. 4

15. What is the Mandalorian's first ship called?

16. What kind of combat vehicle do raiders use to attack the village on Sorgan where Din Djarin and Grogu are staying?
    a. An AAT tank
    b. An AT-ST
    c. An X-wing
    d. An AT-TE walker

17. Kaz says that the *Fireball* looks like "an ____ with wings".
    a. Angel
    b. Explosion
    c. Accident
    d. Excuse

18. What kind of vehicle does Rey use to travel around on Jakku?
    a. AT-ST
    b. Speeder
    c. Tank
    d. X-wing

19. Which ship do Rey and Finn steal to escape from Jakku?

20. True or False? Rey uses the Force to lift the X-wing out of the water around the island on Ahch-To.

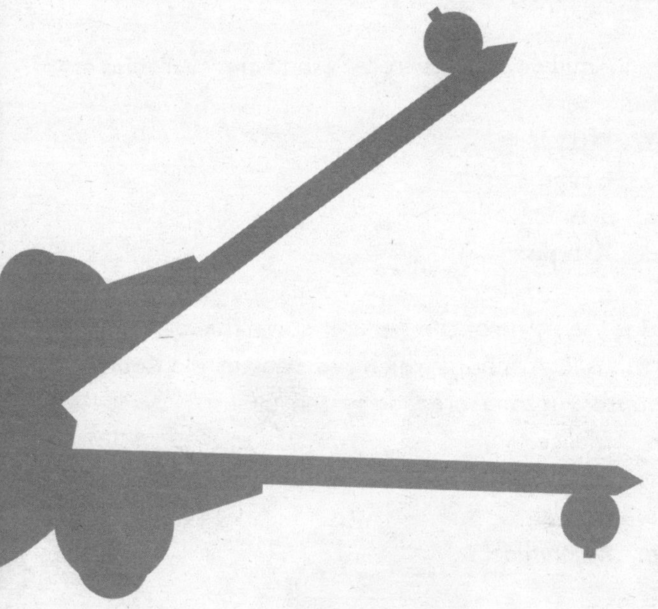

1. Which part of Jar Jar goes numb after he catches it in the energy binders of Anakin's podracer?
   a. His fingers
   b. His feet
   c. His ears
   d. His tongue

2. Queen Amidala escapes from Naboo in a "____ 327 Nubian" starship.
   a. H-type
   b. I-type
   c. J-type
   d. K-type

3. What is the name of the Separatist warship carrying enormous ion cannons which Jedi Master Plo Koon encounters in the Abregado system?
   a. *Malice*
   b. *Malevolence*
   c. *Mauler*
   d. *Magnitude*

4. How many swoops are in Enfys Nest's gang which attacks the conveyex transport?
   a. 3
   b. 4
   c. 5
   d. 6

5. What is the name of the *Ghost*'s small shuttlecraft?

6. What new kind of starfighter prototype does Hera fly on the planet Shantipole?
    a. Fire wing
    b. Blade wing
    c. Laser wing
    d. Hyper wing

7. Cassian and Melshi escape from Narkina 5 aboard what kind of ship?
    a. Corellian YT-1300 freighter
    b. Quadjumper
    c. U-wing
    d. VCX-100 freighter

8. What kind of ship do the rebels use to push one disabled Star Destroyer into another to bring down the shield generator over Scarif?
    a. Y-wing
    b. Hammerhead corvette
    c. Imperial shuttle
    d. Mon Cala cruiser

9. How fast does Han say the *Millennium Falcon* can go past lightspeed?

10. Han tells Luke that "travelling through hyperspace ain't like ____!"

11. What kind of ship does Darth Vader use when he visits the second Death Star while it is under construction?
    a. Lambda shuttle
    b. TIE fighter
    c. TIE bomber
    d. X-wing

12. The juggernaut vehicles used to transport rhydonium on Morak have how many wheels?
    a. 4
    b. 6
    c. 8
    d. 10

13. What kind of ship does Boba Fett fly?

14. Peli say she has what sort of ship as a replacement for the *Razor Crest*?
    a. Naboo N-1 starfighter
    b. X-wing
    c. B-wing
    d. Rogue class starfighter

15. What kind of ship containing a creature Neeku adopts as a pet does Synara salvage from the sea?
    a. X-wing
    b. U-wing
    c. Z-95
    d. T-47

16. What is Hype's callsign within Ace Squadron?

17. Can you name the Resistance starfighter squadron led by Torra's mother?
    a. Quartz Squadron
    b. Jade Squadron
    c. Gold Squadron
    d. Silver Squadron

18. Which squadrons of starfighters does Poe lead during the Battle of Starkiller Base?
    a. Blue and Red
    b. Black and Blue
    c. Red and Green
    d. Gold and Red

19. How many First Order Star Destroyers are already at D'Qar before the dreadnought arrives?
    a. 3
    b. 4
    c. 5
    d. 6

20. What kind of vehicle does Rey use to get to the wreckage of the second Death Star?
    a. Landspeeder
    b. Sea skiff
    c. Ski speeder
    d. X-wing

1. What kind of transport does Boss Nass give the Jedi to make their way through the centre of Naboo?

2. Anakin's ship *Twilight* used to be what kind of freighter?

3. What is the name of Trace Martez's ship?

4. The *Marauder* is a modified version of what kind of ship?

5. What is the name of General Grievous' flagship at the Battle of Coruscant?

6. What kind of vehicle does General Grievous use to try and escape from Obi-Wan on Utapau?

7. What model of ship is the *Millennium Falcon*?

8. What is the name of the Inquisitors' ship which takes them to Tatooine to hunt for Jedi?

9. Luthen is intercepted over Segra Milo by what kind of Imperial ship?

10. What is the callsign of the U-wing Cassian flies to Jedha?

11. What is the name of Admiral Raddus' flagship at the Battle of Scarif?

12. Luke used to practise his piloting in Beggar's Canyon on Tatooine in what kind of ship?

13. What type of starfighter does Darth Vader fly during the Battle of Yavin?

14. What is the name of Admiral Ackbar's flagship at the Battle of Endor?

15. What is the ship called which Han and Chewie use to transport rathtars?

1. Padmé Amidala is the Queen and then Senator of which planet?
    a. Rodia
    b. Alderaan
    c. Corellia
    d. Naboo

2. On which planet does Anakin grow up as a slave?
    a. Hoth
    b. Ord Mantell
    c. Tatooine
    d. Mon Cala

3. What is the name of the planet considered to be the heart and capital of the galaxy?
    a. Ferrix
    b. Coruscant
    c. Utapau
    d. Geonosis

4. On which planet are clone soldiers produced for the Army of the Republic?
    a. Kamino
    b. Ryloth
    c. Eadu
    d. Mandalore

5. Where does Admiral Tarkin send the Bad Batch on a mission to test their loyalty?
    a. Christophsis
    b. Onderon
    c. Felucia
    d. Saleucami

6. Who gives the order to Admiral Rampart to open fire on Tipoca City and destroy it?
    a. The Emperor
    b. Admiral Tarkin
    c. Darth Vader
    d. Grand Admiral Thrawn

7. The Bad Batch take the Wookiee Gungi to which planet after rescuing him from the droid cartel?
    a. Kashyyyk
    b. Ord Mantell
    c. Rodia
    d. Sullust

8. Mustafar is what kind of planet?
    a. Ocean
    b. Desert
    c. Ice
    d. Volcanic

9. On which muddy planet does Han fight as part of the Imperial infantry?
    a. Mon Cala
    b. Bothawui
    c. Takodana
    d. Mimban

10. Han and his companions steal unrefined coaxium from the spice mines of ____?
    a. Teth
    b. Mortis
    c. Kessel
    d. Dathomir

11. Cassian joins a rebel group to steal money from the Empire on which planet?
    a. Aldhani
    b. Alderaan
    c. Abafar
    d. Atollon

12. How many prisoners are there working on each table in the prison on Narkina 5?
    a. 5
    b. 6
    c. 7
    d. 8

13. As a young girl, Princess Leia is kidnapped from which planet?
    a. Tatooine
    b. Alderaan
    c. Lothal
    d. Naboo

14. Which of these places is not located on Tatooine?
    a. Mos Eisley
    b. Aldera
    c. Mos Espa
    d. Mos Pelgo

15. Can you identify which of these is not an ice planet?
    a. Hoth
    b. Ilum
    c. Jakku
    d. Krownest

16. Where does Yoda go to live in exile after the rise of the Empire?
    a. Kashyyyk
    b. Tatooine
    c. Naboo
    d. Dagobah

17. Lando Calrissian is the Baron Administrator of which city on Bespin?
    a. Angel City
    b. Cloud City
    c. Mynock City
    d. Casino City

18. What kind of planet is Castilon?
    a. Gas
    b. Desert
    c. Ocean
    d. Ice

19. On which planet is Rey seemingly abandoned as a child?
    a. Takodana
    b. D'Qar
    c. Jedha
    d. Jakku

20. After the destruction of their base on D'Qar, the remains of the Resistance try to flee to which planet to escape the First Order fleet?
    a. Crait
    b. Ahch-To
    c. Kijimi
    d. Cantonica

1. Qui-Gon suggests that the Queen of Naboo accompanies him to which planet after the Trade Federation invades?
   a. Geonosis
   b. Mustafar
   c. Tatooine
   d. Coruscant

2. Fives and Echo serve together as rookies at a tracking station in which location?
   a. Rishi moon
   b. Felucia
   c. Christophsis
   d. Saleucami

3. Ahsoka and Barriss are tasked to deliver what from Ord Cestus to the battlefront on Dantooine?
   a. Weapons
   b. Food
   c. Medical supplies
   d. Ammunition

4. In his vision from the Son, Anakin sees the destruction of which planet?

5. Where is the first ever sanctioned meeting of representatives of the Republic and the Separatists held?
   a. Coruscant
   b. Ord Mantell
   c. Mandalore
   d. Alderaan

6. Savage Opress' mystical amulet leads him to which planet in his quest to find Maul?
    a. Lotho Minor
    b. Segra Milo
    c. Glee Anselm
    d. Dathomir

7. The featureless deserts of Abafar are also known as what?
    a. The Wastes
    b. The Void
    c. The Desert
    d. The Sea

8. On which planet do the Bad Batch get introduced to Riot Racing?
    a. Anaxes
    b. Iridonia
    c. Serolonis
    d. Nal Hutta

9. Corellia is a planet famous for building what?

10. Kanan and Ezra embark on a mission to rescue Jedi Master Luminara Unduli from which prison?
    a. The Spire
    b. The Citadel
    c. The Maw
    d. The Pit

11. Sabine helps Imperial pilots to defect from which elite TIE pilot training facility?

12. Luthen tries to persuade Saw Gerrera to help with a rebel attack on an Imperial power station in which place?

13. Jyn's father works at the top secret Imperial laboratory on which planet?

14. When she is captured by the Empire near Tatooine, Princess Leia insists that her ship is simply on a diplomatic mission to where?

15. Before the Battle of Endor, the Empire receives reports of a rebel fleet massing near which planet?
    a. Mon Cala
    b. Hoth
    c. Tatooine
    d. Sullust

16. Where does Ahsoka tell Din Djarin that Grogu was raised?

17. Neeku's dream is to live in which part of the *Colossus* platform?

18. Where does Kaz tell Neeku to set as the destination for the *Colossus'* lightspeed jump?
    a. D'Qar
    b. Aeos Prime
    c. Hosnian Prime
    d. Jakku

19. According to Han, what do some people think Luke went looking for after walking away from training a new generation of Jedi?

20. On which planet did Luke's search for Exegol seem to come to an end?

1. What is the capital city of Naboo?
2. Where does Jango Fett say he was hired to become part of the clone trooper programme?
3. On which planet is the Zillo Beast first discovered?
4. What is the capital city of Mandalore?
5. On which planet do the Bad Batch get chased by a swarm of crab-like creatures?
6. The Imperial Navy Academy is on which planet?
7. Cassian is originally from which planet?
8. Cassian goes to hide as a tourist on which planet after the heist on Aldhani?
9. Yoda tells Ezra to find which planet?
10. On which planet does Director Krennic find Galen Erso and his family hiding?
11. Lando says the "little manoeuvre" he made at which battle might be the reason why he was made a rebel general?
12. Din Djarin originally finds Grogu on which planet?

13. Ahsoka tells Din Djarin to take Grogu to the ruins of an old Jedi Temple on which planet?

14. Near which planet does Kaz plan to rendezvous with Norath to join the Resistance?

15. What is the name of the sacred village on Jakku where Poe meets with an old ally of General Leia Organa?

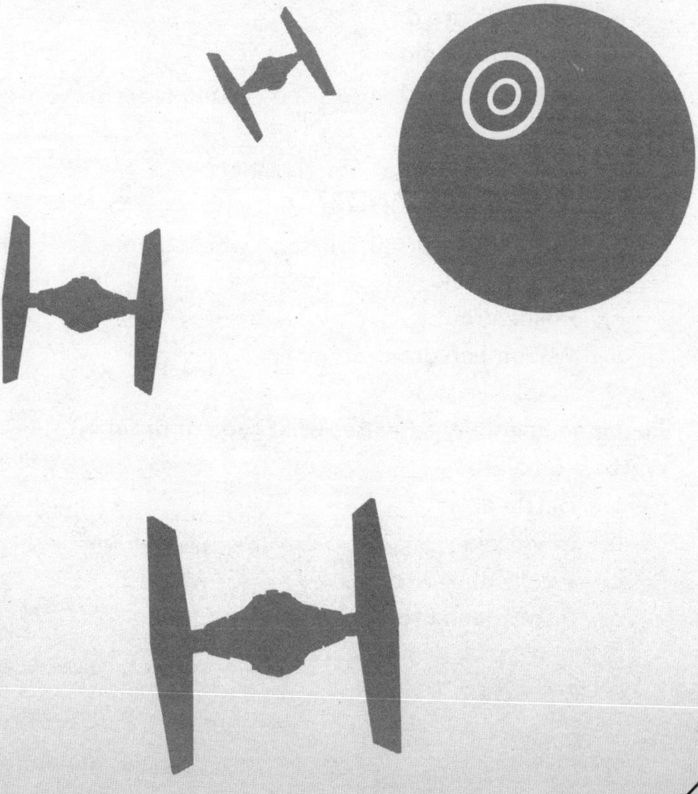

1. What kind of droid welcomes Obi-Wan Kenobi and Qui-Gon Jinn aboard the Trade Federation ship orbiting Naboo?
    a. Battle droid
    b. Protocol droid
    c. Medical droid
    d. Power droid

2. The Trade Federation army which invades Naboo is mostly made up of which kind of droid?
    a. B1 battle droid
    b. B2 battle droid
    c. B3 battle droid
    d. B4 battle droid

3. What kind of droid is R2-D2?
    a. Commando droid
    b. Mouse droid
    c. Police droid
    d. Astromech droid

4. Jar Jar accidentally activates what type of droid in Watto's junkyard?
    a. Battle droid
    b. Spy droid
    c. Pit droid
    d. Astromech droid

5. How many Sith probe droids does Darth Maul launch on Tatooine to hunt for Queen Amidala?
    a. 1
    b. 2
    c. 3
    d. 4

6. Which droid meets Anakin and Padmé when they first arrive at the Lars farm?
   a. R2-D2
   b. R5-D4
   c. C-3PO
   d. TC-14

7. What piece of C-3PO is accidentally removed from his body and attached to a battle droid on Geonosis?
   a. His arm
   b. His foot
   c. His leg
   d. His head

8. What nickname does the Bad Batch's power droid have?
   a. Sparks
   b. Torch
   c. Gonky
   d. Twitch

9. Who fixes Princess Leia's droid, Lola, after it is broken by her kidnappers?
   a. Obi-Wan Kenobi
   b. Anakin Skywalker
   c. Bail Organa
   d. R2-D2

10. What is droid C1-10P better known as?
   a. Bucket
   b. Red
   c. Chopper
   d. Goldie

11. What colour is the astromech droid that Luke and Uncle Owen initially buy from the Jawas instead of R2-D2?
    a. Green and red
    b. Blue and white
    c. Yellow and black
    d. Red and white

12. Which droid runs away from Luke to go looking for Obi-Wan Kenobi on Tatooine?
    a. C-3PO
    b. R5-D4
    c. BB-8
    d. R2-D2

13. What kind of droids does the Empire launch to search for the hidden rebel base after the Battle of Yavin?
    a. Probe droids
    b. Battle droids
    c. Rocket droids
    d. Assassin droids

14. C-3PO tells the supervisor of Jabba the Hutt's droid pool that he is fluent in over how many different forms of communication?
    a. Over 3 million
    b. Over 4 million
    c. Over 5 million
    d. Over 6 million

15. Kuiil repairs and reprogrammes which droid to use as a helper on his farm?
    a. IG-88
    b. EV-9D9
    c. IG-11
    d. 4-LOM

16. Which droid does Poe initially leave behind to help Kaz with his spy mission?
    a. BB-8
    b. CB-23
    c. TC-14
    d. R3-S6

17. What does Yeager call his distinctive co-pilot droid?
    a. Torch
    b. Bolts
    c. Bucket
    d. Sparks

18. On Jakku, Poe gives the piece of the map to Luke Skywalker's location to which droid?
    a. R2-D2
    b. C-3PO
    c. BB-8
    d. D-0

19. What colour is C-3PO's arm when he first meets Han on Takodana?
    a. Gold
    b. Silver
    c. Red
    d. Grey

20. Which malfunctioning part of D-0 does Rey fix?
    a. Bad motivator
    b. Squeaky wheel
    c. Broken antenna
    d. Overloaded power converter

1. When he is activated in his workshop, Anakin's droid introduces himself as "C-3PO, ____".
    a. Etiquette and protocol droid
    b. Human-cyborg relations
    c. Service and translation droid
    d. Interpreter and customs droid

2. What kind of droids guard General Grievous aboard his flagship in the Battle of Coruscant?

3. Which Super Tactical Droid does Count Dooku send to Onderon to help put down the rebel uprising?
    a. General Grievous
    b. General Kalani
    c. General Kraken
    d. General Kallus

4. Which of these droids is not a member of D-Squad?
    a. QT-KT
    b. U9-C4
    c. TC-14
    d. WAC-47

5. Which modification does R2-D2 receive from Dr Gubacher before his mission with D-Squad?

6. Which droid do the Bad Batch find hiding in Nala Se's laboratory when they attempt to rescue Hunter?
   a. R2-D2
   b. QT-KT
   c. AZI-3
   d. CB-23

7. Lando says that L3-37's brain contains the best ____ in the galaxy?

8. What is the full designation of Maarva's groundmech salvage unit?
   a. B2CAS
   b. B2EMO
   c. B2AND
   d. B2MAR

9. Which Inquisitor frequently uses ID9 seeker droids?

10. Ezra and Sabine are given the code phrase "it's a long way to ____" to identify themselves to a secret droid courier which needs escorting to Havok outpost.
    a. Tatooine
    b. Malachor
    c. Lothal
    d. Alderaan

11. What does Han call C-3PO when telling him to hurry up during their escape from the rebel base on Hoth?

12. Chewbacca rescues the parts of C-3PO from which alien species about to disintegrate them on Cloud City?
    a. Rodians
    b. Jawas
    c. Ugnaughts
    d. Anzellans

13. Which part of C-3PO is not completely rebuilt by R2-D2 during the *Millennium Falcon's* escape from Cloud City?

14. Where is R2-D2 told he will be put to work after he is given to Jabba the Hutt as a gift?

15. Which droid does Peli send with Din Djarin on his quest to the Mines of Mandalore?
    a. R4P17
    b. R5-D4
    c. R3-S6
    d. R5-K6

16. Which droid takes over from BB-8 as Kaz's helper?
    a. R2-D2
    b. CB-23
    c. R4-D12
    d. R2-C4

17. What is the name of Venisa Doza's astromech droid?

18. On Jakku, which creature does Rey prevent from capturing BB-8 and using him for parts?

19. How many of Unkar's thugs try to steal BB-8 at Niima outpost?
    a. 2
    b. 3
    c. 4
    d. 5

20. What colour do C-3PO's eyes become when he accesses the translation of the Sith inscription on Ochi's dagger?

1. Cad Bane abducts C-3PO and R2-D2 to gain information on which building?

2. What is the name of Cad Bane's techno-service droid companion?

3. The Separatists deploy which kind of cybernetically enhanced biological weapons during their attack on Mon Cala?

4. What is the name of the Cid's cocky riot racer droid?

5. What is the full designation of the young Princess Leia's droid companion?

6. What kind of droids does Obi-Wan Kenobi encounter patrolling the corridors of Fortress Inquisitorius?

7. According to K-2SO, what is the rebels' percentage chance of failing to successfully fly through the canyons on Eadu?

8. What kind of deadly assassin droid in disguise nearly destroys the rebel base on Atollon?

9. What does C-3PO tell Uncle Owen was his first job?

10. Which two droid bounty hunters does Darth Vader hire to hunt down the *Millennium Falcon*?

11. What is the name of the droid hired to pilot the *Razor Crest* on a mission to free a New Republic prisoner?

12. During the attack on his village as a child, what kind of droid finds Din Djarin when he is hiding?

13. What is the name of the droid inherited from Jabba the Hutt which helps Daimyo Boba Fett with his strategy and diplomacy?

14. What kind of combat droids attack Boba Fett and his allies during the battle in Mos Espa?

15. What is Bucket's full droid designation?

1. What does Obi-Wan throw at Jango Fett's ship as it blasts away from the landing pad on Kamino?
   a. His lightsaber
   b. A thermal detonator
   c. A tracking device
   d. A rock

2. What colour is the blade of Yoda's lightsaber?
   a. Yellow
   b. Green
   c. Blue
   d. White

3. True or False? Jedi Master Kit Fisto needs special equipment to breathe underwater.

4. What material does the youngling Gungi use to make his lightsaber hilt?
   a. Metal
   b. Ice
   c. Wood
   d. Plastic

5. What part of Maul is mechanical when Savage Opress finds him?
   a. Arms
   b. Legs
   c. Hands
   d. Chest

6. What distinctive part of his equipment can the bounty hunter Embo hurl at targets to attack them?
   a. Hat
   b. Shoe
   c. Glove
   d. Shield

7. What colour are Ahsoka's lightsaber blades when Anakin returns them to her after she leaves the Jedi Order?
   a. Green
   b. White
   c. Blue
   d. Yellow

8. Cassian and the other prisoners are making parts for which piece of Imperial technology?
   a. The first Death Star
   b. Star Destroyers
   c. TIE fighters
   d. AT-AT walkers

9. What colour is the laser beam of the Death Star's main weapon?
   a. Red
   b. Green
   c. Blue
   d. White

10. According to Han, "hokey religions and ancient weapons are no match for a good ____ at your side."
    a. Buddy
    b. Blaster
    c. Ship
    d. Co-pilot

11. What does C-3PO leave on the console when he and R2-D2 lock themselves in a storage room on the Death Star to avoid some stormtroopers?
    a. Blaster
    b. Lightsaber
    c. Communicator
    d. Thermal detonator

12. What sort of weapon do the rebels need to use to penetrate the exhaust port on the first Death Star?
    a. Proton torpedoes
    b. Ion cannons
    c. Seismic charges
    d. Turbolasers

13. Which system on the *Millennium Falcon* is deactivated by the Empire to try and prevent the rebels from escaping Bespin?
    a. Shields
    b. Weapons
    c. Navigational computer
    d. Hyperdrive

14. What piece of technology does Din Djarin use to identify his targets?
    a. Bounty scanner
    b. Bounty coder
    c. Bounty puck
    d. Bounty pad

15. What kind of weapon does the Magistrate on Corvus promise Din Djarin in return for ridding them of a troublesome Jedi?
    a. A beskar sword
    b. The Darksaber
    c. A lightsaber
    d. A beskar spear

16. What colour is the blade of Kylo Ren's lightsaber?
    a. White
    b. Red
    c. Yellow
    d. Purple

17. Rey uses what sort of weapon to defend herself from the thugs trying to steal BB-8?
    a. Quarterstaff
    b. Blaster
    c. Blue
    d. White

18. Whose ruined helmet does Kylo Ren occasionally talk to?
    a. Boba Fett
    b. Darth Vader
    c. The Mandalorian
    d. Luke Skywalker

19. Before Rey heads off on her search for Exegol, whose lightsaber does Leia give back to her?
    a. Yoda's
    b. Mace Windu's
    c. Darth Vader's
    d. Luke Skywalker's

20. The clue to the location of the Sith wayfinder is inscribed on what kind of weapon?
    a. Bow
    b. Dagger
    c. Lightsaber
    d. Blaster

1. During the Battle of Coruscant, what do some Separatist missiles drop onto Obi-Wan's starfighter?

2. What does Darth Sidious hire Cad Bane to steal from the Jedi Temple?
    a. A holocron
    b. A lightsaber
    c. A kyber crystal
    d. A datapad

3. Where on their body would you find a clone trooper's identifying code?
    a. On their neck
    b. On their wrist
    c. On their head
    d. On their back

4. Fives persuades AZI-3 to give Tup what sort of scan?

5. What kind of weapon does Omega take from some Zygerrian slavers?
    a. Energy bow
    b. Bowcaster
    c. Energy axe
    d. Blaster

6. What does Haja Estree use to convince people he can move objects with the Force?

7. Which broken piece of technology that belongs to Obi-Wan does Reva find after her battle with Darth Vader?
    a. His lightsaber
    b. His imagecaster
    c. His holocron
    d. His datapad

8. What hidden combat function does Ezra's first lightsaber have?

9. What kind of weapons did Cassian's tribe on Kenari favour using?

10. How much does Cassian want from Luthen for the Starpath Unit he is selling?
    a. 20,000 credits
    b. 30,000 credits
    c. 40,000 credits
    d. 50,000 credits

11. Who tries to hotwire the doors to the Imperial bunker on Endor after R2-D2 is shot and damaged?

12. Who fires the shot that destroys the power regulator on the second Death Star's main reactor?
    a. Lando Calrissian
    b. Nien Nunb
    c. Wedge Antilles
    d. Arvel Crynyd

13. What weapon does Din Djarin use to make the ravinak release his ship?
    a. Energy bow
    b. Amban rifle
    c. The Darksaber
    d. E-11 blaster rifle

14. After making Din Djarin a cuirass, the Armorer uses some of the excess beskar to make what kind of weapon?

15. Which piece of technology does Boba Fett regularly sleep in to heal himself of his wounds from the Sarlacc?

16. Which weapon does Boba Fett use to escape the Sarlacc?
    a. Flamethrower
    b. Thermal detonator
    c. Blaster rifle
    d. Dagger

17. What does Rey wear while she eats and watches space ships heading into orbit on Jakku?

18. Rose says the patrons of Canto Bight got rich selling what to the First Order?
    a. Spice
    b. Weapons
    c. Food
    d. Information

19. Who is responsible for the creation of Supreme Leader Snoke?

20. On Exegol, what does Rey pass to Kylo through their Force connection so he can defeat the Knights of Ren?

1. Apart from money, what else does Jango ask from the Kaminoans as payment for being part of the Clone Trooper programme?

2. How much do the criminals of the Coruscant underworld say it would cost for them to get another lightsaber for Ahsoka after hers is stolen?

3. What is the last number Mace Windu needs to complete the code to deactivate a Separatist bomb on Anaxes?

4. Unrefined coaxium will explode if it drops below what temperature?

5. What kind of weapon were the Lasan Honour Guard known for using?

6. Who forged the Darksaber?

7. Sabine says her Mandalorian armour is how old?

8. What ancient military weapon does Luthen show Mon Mothma in his gallery on Coruscant?

9. What kind of blaster rifle is standard issue for Imperial stormtroopers?

10. What kind of blaster is Han Solo famous for using?

11. What kind of blaster pistol does Din Djarin use?

12. What traditional Tusken weapon does Boba Fett make for himself?

13. The Wookiee Krrsantan is famous for using what kind of brawler weapon?

14. From where does Starkiller Base get power for its weapon?

15. What piece of technology does Leia give Rey so she can find her way back to the Resistance fleet?

1. Which native species lives underwater on Naboo?
    a. Sullustans
    b. Gungans
    c. Quarren
    d. Jawas

2. What species are Hondo Ohnaka and the majority of his pirates?
    a. Trandoshan
    b. Gamorrean
    c. Nikto
    d. Weequay

3. Which two species live on Mon Cala?
    a. Mon Calamari and Dugs
    b. Mon Calamari and Rodians
    c. Mon Calamari and Quarren
    d. Mon Calamari and Twi'leks

4. Karkarodon Ambassador Riff Tamson resembles which kind of creature?
    a. Pig
    b. Shark
    c. Spider
    d. Horse

5. How many legs does an Acklay have?
    a. 2
    b. 4
    c. 6
    d. 8

6. What species is Cid?
    a. Aqualish
    b. Trandoshan
    c. Kaminoan
    d. Bith

7. How long did it take the Empire to drive the native Dhanis out of the highlands?
    a. 5 years
    b. 10 years
    c. 20 years
    d. 100 years

8. Dewbacks are native to which planet?
    a. Kashyyyk
    b. Tatooine
    c. Dantooine
    d. Alderaan

9. What species is Chewbacca?
    a. Wookiee
    b. Klatooinian
    c. Dug
    d. Devaronian

10. Which small creatures from Tatooine did Luke used to hunt in Beggar's Canyon?
    a. Sand rats
    b. Rock rats
    c. Womp rats
    d. Canyon rats

11. What species are Boba Fett's bodyguards when he is Daimyo?
    a. Wookiees
    b. Trandoshans
    c. Gamorreans
    d. Tuskens

12. What creature do both Jabba the Hutt and Boba Fett keep as a pet?
    a. Bantha
    b. Wampa
    c. Gundark
    d. Rancor

13. What species is Kuiil?
    a. Sullustan
    b. Jawa
    c. Ugnaught
    d. Nikto

14. What kind of creature does Din Djarin have to battle to get what he needs to trade with the Jawas for his ship parts?
    a. Gundark
    b. Dewback
    c. Rancor
    d. Mudhorn

15. What creature tunnels through the centre of Mos Pelgo before swallowing a bantha?
    a. Mythosaur
    b. Krayt dragon
    c. Tauntaun
    d. Nexu

16. What other being of a similar species to Grogu does Ahsoka say she has met before?
    a. Greedo
    b. Wicket
    c. Yoda
    d. Zeb

17. What species is Hype Fazon?
    a. Rodian
    b. Mon Calamari
    c. Quarren
    d. Hutt

18. What name do Orka and Flix give the gorg which Kaz buys them?
    a. Binky
    b. Bitey
    c. Blinky
    d. Bestie

19. Which creatures are playing with the lightsaber Luke threw away when Rey finds it?
    a. Porgs
    b. Tooka cats
    c. Gorgs
    d. Corellian hounds

20. What is the name of the black market droidsmith Poe is looking for on Kijimi?
    a. Babu Frik
    b. Vranki
    c. Maz Kanata
    d. Klaud

1. What species is Viceroy Nute Gunray?
    a. Snivvian
    b. Givin
    c. Kubaz
    d. Neimoidian

2. What special ability does the Clawdite Zam Wesell have?

3. What does Dex refer to Kaminoans as when he is talking to Obi-Wan?
    a. Cloners
    b. Soldiers
    c. Scientists
    d. Witches

4. How does the Geonosian Queen Karina the Great control the minds of her drones –and hope to control the minds of Jedi, too?

5. Who is the oldest and wisest of the Nightsister clan?

6. What is the name of the spider-like creatures which the Bad Batch encounter on Kashyyyk?
    a. Netspinners
    b. Netwinders
    c. Netcasters
    d. Netmasters

7. What creature attacks Wrecker in the remains of a Venator-class cruiser on Bracca?
    a. Rancor
    b. Rathtar
    c. Dragonsnake
    d. Dianoga

8. What species is Rio Durant, the pilot on Beckett's crew?
    a. Ardennian
    b. Besalisk
    c. Tognath
    d. Whiphid

9. Zeb Orellios belongs to which alien species that was almost wiped out by the Empire?

10. The blue-skinned Grand Admiral Thrawn is which alien species.
    a. Ortolan
    b. Duros
    c. Chiss
    d. Britarro

11. What is the name of Grand Admiral Thrawn's Noghri assassin?

12. What kind of creature do Rex, Wolffe and Gregor try to catch, using Zeb as bait?
    a. Nerf
    b. Joopa
    c. K'lor'slug
    d. Orray

13. What can be an unfortunate side effect of being exposed to Bor Gullet?

14. Which long-snooted Kubaz summons Imperial troops to stop the *Millennium Falcon* from leaving Tatooine with the droids on board?

15. The mayor of Mos Espa, Mok Shaiz, is which species?

16. What kind of creatures make life miserable for Poe and Kaz when they are investigating a distress call from a freighter in Sector 6?
    a. Jawas
    b. Kowakian monkey-lizards
    c. Womp rats
    d. Anoobas

17. Which kind of creature are Kaz and Griff sentenced to be fed to by the inhabitants of Aeos Prime?
    a. Krakavora
    b. Jakoosk
    c. Bonzami
    d. Mamacore

18. The females of the Lanai species on Ahch-To are also known as what?

19. What kind of creature does Kuiil teach Din Djarin to ride?
    a. Bantha
    b. Blurrg
    c. Ronto
    d. Eopie

20. A group of which alien species betrays Din Djarin and tries to kill him out at sea on Trask?

1. What is the name of the species of winged creature that is both native to the sea and sky on Kamino?

2. Which underwater creature helps Jar Jar rescue Padmé when she is captured on Rodia?

3. What species is Ahsoka?

4. What is the name of the Grindalid head of the White Worms gang on Corellia?

5. What is Dhani for "hello"?

6. What is the name of the Chandrilan drink which can have a worm-like creature dissolved in it?

7. What are the first names of the alien Pamular brothers who capture Cassian and Melshi after their prison breakout?

8. What alien species is the Grand Inquisitor?

9. What do puffer pigs have a gift for detecting?

10. Which spider-like species is native to Atollon?

11. What species are the musicians that are playing in the Tatooine cantina when Obi-Wan and Luke arrive?

12. Who is the chief of the Ewoks in Endor's Ewok village?

13. Which creature breaks through the ice to grab Din Djarin's ship as he is trying to leave a frigid planet in the Outer Rim?

14. Neeku befriends creatures from which alien race that work in the *Colossus*' Engineering Level?

15. How often does the Aki-Aki Festival of the Ancestors take place?

ANSWERS

YOUNGLING

1. d – Naboo
2. c – Qui-Gon Jinn and Obi-Wan Kenobi
3. c – Commander
4. a – Roger, roger!
5. False
6. Amidala
7. b – Jar Jar Binks
8. c – Nass
9. d – Tatooine
10. c – Darth Maul
11. b – Padmé
12. b – A scrapyard
13. c – Protocol droid
14. Blue and red
15. d – orange
16. b – 3
17. b – 5
18. c – Blaster
19. b – Mace Windu
20. It has two blades

PADAWAN

1. b – Darth Sidious
2. c – Droidekas
3. d – Captain Panaka
4. c – Shield generator
5. a – Mos Espa
6. Hit its nose
7. b – 20,000 republic credits

8. a – Shmi
9. An eye
10. A podracer
11. Its midi-chlorian count
12. d – The Boonta Eve Classic
13. b – Come back and free her
14. c – Plo Koon
15. Bring balance to the Force
16. Suffering
17. In a starfighter cockpit
18. c – Anakin
19. False
20. Valorum

JEDI MASTER

1. TC-14
2. Nute Gunray
3. Dioxis
4. Captain Tarpals
5. Ric Olié
6. Three years old
7. Gardulla the Hutt
8. T-14
9. 7 wupiupi
10. Malastare
11. Over 20,000
12. Anakin and Quadinaros
13. Aurra Sing
14. Bail Antilles or Ainlee Teem
15. Bravo Flight

YOUNGLING

1. a – 1000 years
2. c – Obi-Wan Kenobi
3. d – Yellow
4. His lightsaber
5. b – Jar Jar Binks
6. b – Love
7. Younglings
8. d – Oceans
9. c – A clone army
10. b – His mother
11. a – Watto
12. True
13. c – 4
14. d – Purple
15. c – Destruction
16. c – Boba Fett
17. d – Blue
18. a – Padmé
19. b – His right arm
20. c – Naboo

PADAWAN

1. c – Count Dooku
2. Soldiers
3. b – 10 years
4. d – Death sticks
5. Toxic dart
6. c – Arrogant
7. b – Lama Su

8. b – 2
9. c – 200,000
10. a – Tyranus
11. Seismic charges
12. d – Stepbrother
13. d – Tusken Raiders
14. The Republic
15. c – Jar Jar Binks
16. Padmé
17. The Death Star
18. Force lightning
19. c – Yoda
20. R2-D2 and C-3PO

JEDI MASTER

1. Cordé
2. Zam Wesell
3. Jocasta Nu
4. The Rishi Maze
5. Taun We
6. Jedi Master Sifo-Dyas
7. Almost 10 years ago
8. Shaak
9. Half the time
10. Less than a parsec
11. Poggle the lesser
12. Nexu, reek and acklay
13. Kit Fisto and Ki-Adi Mundi
14. It is out of rockets
15. Lord Tyranus

YOUNGLING

1. a – Snips
2. d – Fives
3. c – Clankers
4. a – Asajj Ventress
5. b – Jar Jar
6. b – Blue Shadow Virus
7. c – The Force
8. c – Mandalore
9. b – The Darksaber
10. c – Boba Fett
11. d – ARC troopers
12. a – Savage Opress
13. b – Chewbacca
14. c – Gungans
15. c – 4
16. d – D-Squad
17. c – Shadow Collective
18. a – Barriss Offee
19. a – Yellow
20. c – Her lightsaber

PADAWAN

1. b – Luminara and Ahsoka
2. a – 1 million credits in spice
3. Droid poppers
4. b – Cham Syndulla
5. b – Ziro the Hutt
6. Tera Sinube
7. Concordia

8. Stealth ship
9. c – Domino
10. b – Aurra Sing
11. Mother Talzin
12. a – Mortis
13. The Citadel
14. b – Hardcase
15. c – 50,000
16. Ilum
17. Duchess Satine
18. d – Skako Minor
19. Loyalty
20. Darth Vader

JEDI MASTER

1. CT-7567
2. 212th
3. Plo Koon
4. Brother
5. Felucia
6. The Kyber Crystal
7. One year
8. Onaconda Farr
9. Dr Boll
10. The memories of people who have touched them
11. Lars Quell
12. Patience
13. Professor Huyang
14. Tup
15. 8108

YOUNGLING

1. General Grievous
2. c – Chancellor Palpatine
3. c – 3
4. d – Oil
5. Lightsabers
6. d – She is pregnant
7. False
8. b – Utapau
9. d – Unnatural
10. d – 4
11. Heart
12. Mace Windu
13. Red
14. Darth Vader
15. a – The Temple
16. False
17. d – R2-D2
18. Obi-Wan
19. Luke and Leia
20. The Death Star

PADAWAN

1. Yellow
2. b – Droids
3. Hit its center eye
4. Sith Lords
5. a – Chancellor Palpatine
6. Naboo
7. d – Chancellor Palpatine

8. d – Passion
9. c – Darth Plagueis
10. d – Count Dooku
11. c – 5
12. c – Treason
13. Order 66
14. Bail Organa
15. Chewbacca and Tarfful
16. d – Bail Organa
17. The first Galactic Empire
18. Darkness
19. Luke
20. Anakin himself

JEDI MASTER

1. Oddball
2. Pride
3. Ray shields
4. 10
5. Create life
6. His apprentice killed him in his sleep
7. Varactyl
8. Kit Fisto, Saesee Tiin and Agen Kolar
9. Agen Kolar
10. Commander Cody
11. 913
12. Mygeeto
13. Plo Koon
14. Polis Massa
15. Qui-Gon Jinn

YOUNGLING

1. d – Clone Force 99
2. c – Follow orders
3. b – Crosshair
4. d- Rampart
5. a – Cid
6. c – Wrecker
7. d – Cad Bane
8. False
9. b – Light
10. c – 1,000
11. a – Hunter
12. True
13. b – Number
14. d – Count Dooku
15. a – Mountain
16. a – Gungi
17. c – Rex
18. b – Echo
19. c – Food
20. d – Tech

PADAWAN

1. b – *Marauder*
2. c – Admiral Tarkin
3. c – Nexu
4. b – Bib Fortuna
5. A tactical droid
6. Mantell Mix
7. b – Taun We

8. A new refinery
9. b – Orn Free Taa
10. Hunter's comlink
11. AZI-3
12. a – Imperial fleet ship types
13. Plan Double Zero
14. Left
15. b – Forged chain codes
16. Admiral Rampart's Defense Recruitment Bill
17. c – Rex
18. Pantora
19. b – Imperial stormtroopers
20. Zillo beast

JEDI MASTER

1. Caleb Dume
2. 11
3. Lula
4. Project War-Mantle
5. Bracca
6. Alpha
7. Dejarik
8. Uncle Gobi
9. 32 rotations
10. Ciddarin Scaleback
11. Octomorph
12. 79's
13. Level 1313
14. Dr Hemlock
15. Eriadu

YOUNGLING

1. a – Corellia
2. c – Qi’ra
3. a – A rock
4. d – A pilot
5. c – Lucky dice
6. b – A hat
7. d – Beckett
8. b – Wookiee
9. True
10. b – Their legs
11. c – Lando
12. c – Wonderful
13. *Millennium Falcon*
14. d – Predictable
15. d – Capes
16. c – Chewbacca and Han
17. a – Restraining bolt
18. b – 12
19. d – Beckett
20. Han

PADAWAN

1. c- White worms
2. d – Moloch
3. c – *Coronet*
4. a – 1
5. b – Order
6. Infantry
7. b – A mind of his own

8. b – Captain
9. b – Moof-milker
10. b – Enfys Nest
11. a – Crimson Dawn
12. Tobias
13. d – Kessel
14. b – L3-37
15. b – 20%
16. b – Lando
17. d – Slaves
18. b – 20
19. Maul
20. Sabacc

JEDI MASTER

1. Lady Proxima
2. The Silo
3. M-68
4. Crimson Dawn or the Hutt Cartel
5. Bossk
6. Valachord
7. Scarif or Mercy Island
8. Pyke Syndicate
9. Savareen
10. A VCX-100
11. Green sylop
12. Thread through Si'Klaata Cluster and then pass through Maelstrom
13. Teräs käsi
14. 190 years old
15. About 60 million credits

YOUNGLING

1. b – 10 years
2. c – 3
3. d – Jedi
4. c – Red
5. c – Obi-Wan Kenobi
6. b – Meat
7. a – Ben
8. c – Lola
9. False
10. c – Make her float
11. d – The Force
12. a – His fear
13. b – Lord Vader
14. a – Stormtroopers
15. a – The Path
16. b – Reva
17. a – In Lola
18. d – Leia
19. True
20. c – Rocks

PADAWAN

1. a – Patience
2. b – Third Sister
3. b – A T-16 skyhopper toy
4. a – Nari
5. c – Vermin
6. c – Organa
7. His and Anakin's lightsabers

8. d – Reva
9. d – Spice
10. b – Haja
11. d – Tawl
12. Anakin Skywalker is alive
13. c – Anakin Skywalker
14. Tala
15. Eyes
16. A tomb of Jedi and Force-sensitive people
17. b – Wade
18. Red
19. c – A holster
20. Qui-Gon Jinn

JEDI MASTER

1. Tibidon sand whale
2. Breha
3. Vect
4. A clone trooper veteran
5. 800 credits
6. Sabacc card
7. Mining
8. Fortress Inquisitorius
9. Luma
10. Quinlan Vos
11. Vintrium crystals
12. Roken
13. Florrum
14. Garel
15. Tuskens

YOUNGLING

1. d – Ezra Bridger
2. b – Lothal
3. c – Sabine
4. b – Obi-Wan Kenobi
5. a – Fulcrum
6. c – The Grand Inquisitor
7. b – Blue
8. False
9. c – Phoenix Squadron
10. c – Ahsoka Tano
11. d – Cold
12. c – Fifth Brother
13. c – Leia
14. b – Agent Kallus
15. c – Maul
16. a – Grand Admiral Thrawn
17. a – The Chosen One
18. True
19. c – TIE defender
20. b – His parents

PADAWAN

1. Garazeb Orellios
2. a – A meiloorun fruit
3. b – Dev Morgan
4. Empire Day
5. d – Cikatro Vizago
6. Tarkintown
7. Rex

8. a – Ketsu Onyo
9. Concord Dawn
10. b – His kindness
11. a – Chopper Base
12. Darth Vader
13. Bendu
14. c – Kalani
15. c – Dathomir
16. Dantooine
17. d – Purple
18. A giant kyber crystal
19. c – Loth-wolves
20. b – All time and space

JEDI MASTER

1. Spectre-5
2. A holodisk with an image of his family
3. A puffer pig
4. Quarrie
5. *Shadow Caster*
6. The Third Battle of Mygeeto
7. Lira San
8. Twin suns
9. Wedge Antilles and Hobbie Klivian
10. Kalikori
11. Gar Saxon
12. Ahsoka Tano and Agent Kallus
13. Caleb Dume
14. A convor
15. Purrgil

YOUNGLING

1. d – Andor
2. c – His sister
3. a – Ferrix
4. d – Red
5. b – Maarva
6. d – Bix
7. b – Coruscant
8. a – Clem
9. c – 7
10. b – His mother
11. c – Mon Mothma
12. b – 3
13. d – Jobs
14. c – 6 years
15. b – Boots and shoes
16. On program!
17. b – White and orange
18. c – Daughters
19. b – Cassian
20. c – Bricks

PADAWAN

1. Morlana One
2. d – Kassa
3. b – N-S9 Starpath Unit
4. c – Fest
5. Luthen Rael
6. b – Timm
7. a – Steergard

8. c – 16
9. An entire sector
10. c – Imperial Security Bureau
11. a – Blue sky kyber
12. The Eye of Aldhani
13. d – Uncle Harlo
14. d – Echo-One
15. a – Taramyn
16. b – Goat hides
17. His manifesto
18. b – Narkina 5
19. 400,000 credits
20. Syril

JEDI MASTER

1. Salman Paak
2. Kerri
3. He was a cook
4. 5 months
5. Kleya
6. Akti Amaugh, the Valley of Caves
7. Every 3 years
8. Sipo Youth Center
9. Frezno
10. 80 million credits
11. 5-2-D
12. Kino Loy
13. Melshi
14. Alderaan 12912505
15. Corv

YOUNGLING

1. b – Director
2. d – Black
3. c – Galen
4. b – Stardust
5. c – 6
6. b – The Force
7. b – Erso
8. d – Jedha
9. d – K-2SO
10. c – Captain
11. b – In his boot
12. a – Kyber crystals
13. a – A knife
14. a – Eadu
15. d – Darth Vader
16. d – Hope
17. d – Cassian says he has to
18. Rogue One
19. d – Force
20. d – Chirrut

PADAWAN

1. b – Lyra
2. d – Saw Gerrera
3. a – Lyra
4. a – Wobani
5. c – A planet killer
6. Bodhi Rook
7. Rebel Intelligence

8. c – 15 years
9. Bor Gullet
10. d – Jyn
11. d – Whills
12. Temple of the Kyber
13. Lightsabers
14. Citadel Tower
15. a – 6
16. b – SW-0608
17. d – Raddus
18. c – Blue squadron
19. 100
20. Bistan

JEDI MASTER

1. Toy stormtrooper doll
2. 20 years
3. Ring of Kafrene
4. A shovel
5. Liana Hallik
6. Strategic analysis
7. *Dauntless*
8. 16
9. General Draven
10. Spies, saboteurs and assassins
11. 2
12. 9
13. 33%
14. c – Darksaber
15. Ion torpedoes

YOUNGLING

1. b – R2-D2
2. c – The Death Star
3. d – Obi-Wan Kenobi
4. Leia Organa
5. White
6. a – Tatooine
7. False
8. d – Blue
9. d – Jawas
10. False
11. Blue
12. a – Luke's father
13. Blue
14. *Millennium Falcon*
15. b – 10,000 credits
16. False
17. b – Moon
18. Red
19. d – Red
20. a – 2

PADAWAN

1. a – *Tantive IV*
2. d – Tosche Station
3. d – Beru and Owen
4. c – Banthas
5. a – General
6. Mos Eisley
7. 94

8. c – Jabba the Hutt
9. a – A piece of junk
10. d – Dantooine
11. The smuggling compartment under the floor
12. TK-421
13. a – Turns off the tractor beams
14. The garbage chute
15. c – Walking carpet
16. Yavin 4
17. b – 2 metres
18. d – Biggs
19. d – 6
20. c – Han and Luke

JEDI MASTER

1. c – *Devastator*
2. Captain Antilles
3. Out beyond the Dune Sea
4. It has a bad motivator
5. Bocce
6. Tusken Raiders
7. Dewbacks
8. Dr Evazan and Ponda Baba
9. Figrin D'an and the Modal Nodes
10. 17,000 credits
11. Grand Moff Wilhuff Tarkin
12. Dianoga
13. Leve 5, Detention Block AA-23. Cell 2187.
14. General Jan Dodonna
15. Luke Skywalker and Wedge Antilles

YOUNGLING

1. c- Hoth
2. d – Tauntauns
3. c – Obi-Wan Kenobi
4. d – Dagobah
5. Nerf herder
6. a – Into an asteroid field
7. R2-D2
8. c – It sinks into the swamp
9. False
10. False
11. c – Excitement
12. b – Try
13. a – Boba Fett
14. Lando Calrissian
15. False
16. d – Chewbacca
17. c – Han Solo
18. d – I know
19. Right
20. False

PADAWAN

1. d – 6th
2. c – Echo Base
3. b – Highnesses
4. b – Commander
5. a – Wampa
6. b – Ion cannon
7. a – Ozzel

8. AT-ST
9. Luke Skywalker
10. False
11. b – Its hyperdrive motivator is damaged
12. b – 4
13. b – A lamp
14. b – Mudhole
15. Obi-Wan Kenobi
16. d – Reckless
17. Darth Vader
18. d – Bespin
19. Boba Fett
20. True

JEDI MASTER

1. Echo 3
2. *Executor*
3. Ord Mantell
4. Pull the ears off a gundark
5. North Ridge
6. Dak Ralter
7. 3,720 to 1
8. 800 years
9. Mynocks
10. 6
11. Disintegrations
12. Platform 327
13. Tibanna gas
14. Lobot
15. Luke's hatred

YOUNGLING

1. d – The Emperor
2. a – 2
3. c – C-3PO and R2-D2
4. d – A thermal detonator
5. b – Leia
6. False
7. c – A skull
8. c – 1,000 years
9. b – 2
10. d – R2-D2
11. Green
12. d – Han
13. Red
14. c – Endor
15. b – Darth Vader
16. a – Wicket
17. a – Chewbacca
18. b – God
19. d – Twin sister
20. c – A statue

PADAWAN

1. b – More men
2. Bib Fortuna
3. c – 50,000
4. Blindness
5. Mind trick
6. Rancor
7. a – Her chains

8. c – Eye
9. 900
10. Admiral Ackbar
11. a – Lando
12. d – Fly casual
13. Princess Leia
14. Food
15. An entire legion
16. b – Gold Leader
17. Logs
18. c – 6
19. a – The radar dish
20. d – Yoda, Anakin Skywalker and Obi-Wan Kenobi

JEDI MASTER

1. Jerjerrod
2. Kowakian monkey-lizard
3. In the Great Pit of Carkoon
4. Oola
5. Boushh
6. Bothan spies
7. *Tydirium*
8. Nien Nunb
9. Sanctuary Moon
10. How far is it to the shield generator?
11. Sad
12. Paploo
13. His overconfidence
14. The Empire is jamming them
15. MV-7

YOUNGLING

1. Beskar
2. b – Cold
3. b – Their helmet
4. d – Greef Karga
5. d – Kuiil
6. c – IG-11
7. a – Jawas
8. c – The Egg
9. This is the Way
10. b – Fennec Shand
11. False
12. c – 3
13. d – Grogu
14. a – Moff Gideon
15. a – IG-11
16. b – The Darksaber
17. True
18. a – Bo-Katan Kryze
19. Ahsoka Tano
20. True

PADAWAN

1. c – 50 years old
2. Self-destruct
3. c – Weapons
4. Sooga!
5. A sliver ball from a lever
6. b – Some binocs
7. c – Eat him

8. a – Creed
9. c – Mudhorn
10. c – A jetpack
11. Magic hand thing
12. Cobb Vanth
13. c – Watch
14. b – Corvus
15. Dark troopers
16. Luke Skywalker
17. b – 2
18. b – L52
19. c – Himself
20. a – IG-11

JEDI MASTER

1. The Mythosaur
2. 2
3. The Twi'lek healing baths
4. Toro Calican
5. Migs Mayfeld
6. An E-web heavy repeating blaster
7. The Mining Collective
8. A camtono of silicax crystals
9. An idiot's array
10. Grogu's blood
11. The location of Grand Admiral Thrawn
12. His chain code
13. Alamites
14. Kelleran Beq
15. Paz Vizsla

YOUNGLING

1. d – Tatooine
2. a – Jabba the Hutt
3. b – Fennec Shand
4. d – Jawas
5. d – Tuskens
6. Mos Espa
7. Green
8. c – Cousins
9. a – Speeder bikes
10. b – Water
11. c – Rock
12. His armour
13. c – 10,000 years
14. c – His spear
15. b – For removing his helmet
16. c – 2
17. d – Din Djarin
18. b – The Sanctuary
19. False
20. b – Grogu

PADAWAN

1. Daimyo
2. c – Respect
3. d – 6
4. Krrsantan
5. a – Spice
6. b – 3
7. Rancor

8. Witches of Dathomir
9. His ship
10. b – Loyalty
11. b – His leg
12. A Mandalorian covert
13. c – A Thousand Tears
14. b – Paz Vizsla
15. Mandalore
16. False
17. d – Cad Bane
18. Freetown
19. Beskar chain mail
20. b – Pyke Syndicate

JEDI MASTER

1. Massiff
2. Dokk Strassi
3. Mok Shaiz
4. Garsa Fwip
5. The Order of the Night Wind
6. A Gladiator
7. 1,300 credits
8. Kintan Striders
9. A mod parlor near Mos Eisley
10. Trandoshans
11. Max Rebo
12. Kolzoc Alley
13. A camtono
14. Yoda's
15. R2-D2

YOUNGLING

1. d – Poe
2. Kazuda Xiono
3. b – Castilon
4. c – *Colossus*
5. d – Green
6. a – *Fireball*
7. Flix and Orka
8. False
9. c – Captain Phasma
10. c – Gold
11. a – Synara
12. d – Circle
13. c – 6
14. a – A hyperdrive
15. b – Kaz
16. True
17. b – Kaztastrophe
18. c – Dragons
19. c – General Hux
20. c – The *Fireball*

PADAWAN

1. b – Senator
2. Hype Fazon
3. c – Major Vonreg
4. a – Coruscant
5. c – Hot sauce
6. c – 20,000 credits
7. Kel and Eila

8. b – Guavian Death Gang
9. a – Buggles
10. An Imperial uniform
11. d – Lone Wolf
12. b – Hosnian Prime
13. 20 years
14. a – Lieutenant Galek
15. A Sith temple
16. Hotel and Casino
17. *Titan*
18. d – Ax Tagrin
19. a – Aeos Prime
20. Its engines

JEDI MASTER

1. C4
2. Grevel
3. 387:1
4. Bolza Grool
5. Pure aurodium
6. Hype Fazon, Griff Halloran, Freya Fenris, Bo Keevil and Torra Doza
7. Backwards tailslide
8. Station Theta Black
9. Dedlanite
10. About 3 parsecs
11. DT-533
12. Griff
13. Cantina singer
14. Leoz
15. Sidon Ithano

YOUNGLING

1. b – Luke
2. The First Order
3. d – Jakku
4. Poe
5. c – White and orange
6. False
7. TIE fighter
8. c – Finn
9. d – The Resistance
10. b – Rey
11. c – Home
12. d – Rey
13. a – Starkiller Base
14. b – Snoke
15. b – A lightsaber
16. Kylo
17. d – R2-D2
18. b – Black Leader
19. Chewbacca
20. True

PADAWAN

1. Captain Phasma
2. 3
3. b – Unkar Plutt
4. d – Antenna
5. b – 2
6. Poe's jacket
7. a – Happabore

8. c – Quadjumper
9. Garbage
10. d – D'Qar
11. 14
12. c – Rathtars
13. c – 6
14. c – Ball
15. Maz Kanata
16. d – Chewbacca
17. b – Finn
18. Traitor
19. Darth Vader
20. Captain Phasma

JEDI MASTER

1. Lor San Tekka
2. His blaster
3. Niima outpost
4. Imperial AT-AT walker
5. The Kelvin Ridge and the Sinking Fields
6. 60 portions
7. It puts too much stress on the hyperdrive
8. King Prana
9. Guavian Death Gang and Kanjiklub
10. 50,000 credits
11. Hosnian Prime
12. Snap Wexley
13. Nien Nunb
14. Precinct 47
15. 7

YOUNGLING

1. a – General Hux
2. False
3. b – 1
4. b – Throws it away
5. c – Chewbacca
6. b – Hope
7. d – To die
8. c – Finn
9. c – 3
10. a – Rose
11. b – Blasts him
12. b – A rock
13. c – BB-8
14. True
15. Blue
16. c – Yoda
17. b – Gold
18. c – Snoke
19. c – Captain Phasma
20. b – Red

PADAWAN

1. c – Weapons systems
2. a – Paige
3. b – Porgs
4. Rey
5. c – An X-wing
6. b – Mask

7. Leia's message to Obi-Wan asking for help to deliver the Death Star plans to the rebels.
8. b – Vice Admiral Holdo
9. b – Maz
10. Canto Bight
11. a – Fathiers
12. b – 13
13. Herself
14. b – Failure
15. A waste bin
16. Admiral Holdo
17. Luke
18. a – Jakku
19. Salt
20. Han's lucky dice

JEDI MASTER

1. 1
2. "Finn naked leaking bag!"
3. Thala-siren
4. About 6 minutes (1 system cycle)
5. 18 hours
6. A red plom bloom
7. Slowen Lo
8. Some boots
9. Haysian smelt
10. BB-9E
11. Vulptices
12. The Death Star
13. The mono-ski
14. 13
15. 15,428 to 1

YOUNGLING

1. d- Emperor Palpatine
2. c – R2-D2
3. b – Luke Skywalker
4. c – Kites
5. d – Her necklace
6. a – Poe
7. b – Fly
8. b – Sith
9. d – Chewbacca
10. Left
11. a – Alone
12. True
13. b – General Hux
14. c – Grand daughter
15. c – Han
16. a – R2-D2
17. c – Lando and Chewbacca
18. d – Red
19. d – Yellow
20. c – Skywalker

PADAWAN

1. c – Exegol
2. b – A fleet of Star Destroyers
3. b – The Final Order
4. d – A droid
5. Knights of Ren
6. a – Her family name

7. 2
8. d – Coloured smoke
9. A dagger
10. Left
11. d – Herself
12. D-O
13. c – Spice runner
14. Endor
15. c – Vader's helmet
16. b – Dyad
17. a – Jannah
18. b – Ahch-To
19. TIE fighter
20. Luke and Leia's lightsaber

JEDI MASTER

1. Boolio
2. Ajan Kloss
3. Both sub-alternators
4. Aki-Aki Festival of the Ancestors
5. Ochi of Bestoon
6. Vexis
7. The Pits of Griq
8. Kijimi
9. The Colonies
10. Delta 3-6, transient 9-3-6, bearing 3-2
11. Kef Bir
12. TZ-1719
13. Wedge Antilles
14. Han's medal from the Battle of Yavin
15. Gold system

YOUNGLING

1. c – Yellow
2. c – AT-TE walkers
3. b – White and blue
4. d – Ghost
5. d – Sandcrawler
6. c – 3
7. b – Star Destroyers
8. d – Gold
9. b – TIE fighters
10. b – Armoured
11. b – 4
12. c – X-wing
13. a – A-wing
14. b – 2
15. *Razor Crest*
16. b – An AT-ST
17. b – Explosion
18. b – Speeder
19. *Millennium Falcon*
20. False

PADAWAN

1. d – His tongue
2. c – J-type
3. b – *Malevolence*
4. c – 5
5. *Phantom*
6. b – Blade wing

7. b – Quadjumper
8. b – Hammerhead corvette
9. 0.5 past lightspeed
10. Dustin' crops
11. a – Lambda shuttle
12. d – 10
13. Firespray gunship
14. a – Naboo N-1 starfighter
15. c – Z-95
16. Ace One
17. b – Jade Squadron
18. a – Blue and Red
19. a – 3
20. b – Sea skiff

JEDI MASTER

1. Bongo submarine
2. Spice freighter
3. *Silver Angel*
4. *Omicron*-class attack shuttle
5. *Invisible Hand*
6. Tsmeu-6 wheel bike
7. Corellian YT-1300 freighter
8. *Scythe*
9. *Cantwell*-class Arrestor cruiser
10. LMTR-20
11. *Profundity*
12. T-16 skyhopper
13. TIE Advanced x1
14. *Home One*
15. *Eravana*

YOUNGLING

1. d – Naboo
2. c – Tatooine
3. b – Coruscant
4. a – Kamino
5. b – Onderon
6. b – Admiral Tarkin
7. a – Kashyyyk
8. d – Volcanic
9. d – Mimban
10. c – Kessel
11. a – Aldhani
12. c – 7
13. b – Alderaan
14. b – Aldera
15. c – Jakku
16. d – Dagobah
17. b – Cloud City
18. c – Ocean
19. d – Jakku
20. a – Crait

PADAWAN

1. d – Coruscant
2. a – Rishi moon
3. c – Medical supplies
4. Alderaan
5. c – Mandalore
6. a – Lotho Minor

7. b – The Void
8. Serolonis
9. Starships
10. a – The Spire
11. Skystrike Academy
12. Spellhaus
13. Eadu
14. Alderaan
15. d – Sullust
16. In the Jedi Temple on Coruscant
17. Doza Tower
18. a – D'Qar
19. The first Jedi Temple
20. Pasaana

JEDI MASTER

1. Theed
2. On one of the moons of Bogden
3. Malastare
4. Sundari
5. Aynaboni
6. Carida
7. Kenari
8. Niamos
9. Malachor
10. Lah'mu
11. The Battle of Taanab
12. Arvala-7
13. Tython
14. Batuu
15. Tuanul

YOUNGLING

1. b – Protocol droid
2. a – B1 battle droid
3. d – Astromech droid
4. c – Pit droid
5. c – 3
6. c – C-3PO
7. d – His head
8. c – Gonky
9. a – Obi-Wan Kenobi
10. c – Chopper
11. d – Red and white
12. d – R2-D2
13. a – Probe droids
14. d – Over 6 million
15. c – IG-11
16. a – BB-8
17. c – Buckets
18. c – BB-8
19. c – Red
20. b – Squeaky wheel

PADAWAN

1. b – Human-cyborg relations
2. MagnaGuards
3. b – General Kalani
4. c – TC-14
5. Advanced rocket boosters
6. c – AZI-3

7. Navigational database
8. b – B2EMO
9. Seventh Sister
10. d – Alderaan
11. Goldenrod
12. c – Ugnaughts
13. His leg
14. On Jabba's sail barge
15. b – R5-D4
16. b – CB-23
17. Torch
18. Teedo
19. a – 2
20. Red

JEDI MASTER

1. The Senate Building on Coruscant
2. Todo 360
3. Hydroid Medusas
4. TAY-0
5. L0-LA59
6. ID10 seekers
7. 26%
8. E-XD infiltrator droid
9. Programming binary load lifters
10. IG-88 and 4-LOM
11. Q9-0
12. B2-RP super battle droid
13. 8D8
14. Scorpenek droids
15. R1-J5

YOUNGLING

1. c – A tracking device
2. b – Green
3. False
4. c – Wood
5. b – Legs
6. a – Hat
7. c – Blue
8. a – The first Death Star
9. b – Green
10. b – Blaster
11. c – Communicator
12. a – Proton torpedoes
13. d – Hyperdrive
14. c – Bounty puck
15. d – A beskar spear
16. b – Red
17. a – Quarterstaff
18. b – Darth Vader
19. d – Luke Skywalker's
20. b – Dagger

PADAWAN

1. Buzz droids
2. a – A holocron
3. b – On their wrist
4. Atomic brain scan
5. a – Energy bow
6. Remotes and magnets

7. b – His imagecaster
8. It can fire stun blasts
9. Blowpipes and darts
10. c – 40,000 credits
11. Han
12. c – Wedge Antilles
13. b – Amban rifle
14. Whistling Birds
15. Bacta tank
16. a – Flamethrower
17. A salvaged X-wing pilot helmet
18. b – Weapons
19. Emperor Palpatine
20. A lightsaber

JEDI MASTER

1. An unaltered clone for himself
2. 20,000 credits
3. 7
4. 35 standard
5. AB-75 bo-rifle
6. Tarre Vizsla
7. 500 years old
8. An Utapaun monk cudgel
9. E-11 blaster rifle
10. DL-44 blaster pistol
11. IB-94 blaster pistol
12. A Gaderffii Stick (or Gaffi stick)
13. Knuckle dusters
14. The star of the system it's in
15. A cloaked binary beacon

YOUNGLING

1. b – Gungans
2. d – Weequay
3. c – Mon Calamari and Quarren
4. b – Shark
5. c – 6
6. b – Trandoshan
7. b – 10 years
8. b – Tatooine
9. a – Wookiee
10. c – Womp rats
11. c – Gamorreans
12. d – Rancor
13. c – Ugnaught
14. d – Mudhorn
15. b – Krayt dragon
16. c – Yoda
17. a – Rodian
18. b – Bitey
19. a – Porgs
20. a – Babu Frik

PADAWAN

1. d – Neimoidian
2. Shape-shifting
3. a – Cloners
4. Brain worms
5. Old Daka
6. c – Netcasters

7. d – Dianoga
8. a – Ardennian
9. Lasat
10. c – Chiss
11. Rukh
12. b – Joopa
13. Losing your mind
14. Garindan
15. Ithorian
16. b – Kowakian monkey-lizards
17. a – Krakavora
18. Caretakers
19. b – Blurrg
20. Quarren

JEDI MASTER

1. Aiwha
2. Kwazel maw
3. Togruta
4. Lady Proxima
5. Nahrvai
6. Squig
7. Freedi and Dewi
8. Pau'an
9. Precious minerals
10. Krykna
11. Bith
12. Chief Chirpa
13. Ravinak
14. Chelidae
15. Once every 42 years

NOTES

NOTES

NOTES

NOTES

NOTES